THE AUDUBON
NATURE
ENCYCLOPEDIA

THE AUDUBON
NATURE
ENCYCLOPEDIA

SPONSORED BY THE NATIONAL AUDUBON SOCIETY

VOLUME 7

MO-OR

CURTIS BOOKS
A division of
The Curtis Publishing Company
Philadelphia — New York

CREATED AND PRODUCED BY
COPYLAB PUBLISHING COUNSEL, INC., NEW YORK

PICTORIAL ACKNOWLEDGMENTS, Volume 7

Pat Kirpatrick*, VIII —Allan D. Cruickshank*, 1195, 1206-07, 1230 bottom, 1231, 1239, 1252, 1266, 1276, 1284-85, 1286-87, 1350, 1351, 1374, 1377 bottom, 1381, 1382, 1383, 1384, 1388 —N. E. Beck, Jr.*, 1196 —Russ Kinne*, 1197 —Robert C. Hermes*, 1201, 1202 —United States Department of Agriculture, 1203 —W. D. Berry, 1205, 1249 —John H. Gerard*, 1208 —Lynwood M. Chace*, 1209 left and right —Grace A. Thompson,* 1210 —New York State Conservationist, 1212-13, 1216, 1217, 1218, 1294-95, 1310-11, 1312-13, 1339 —Hugh Spencer*, 1214 —Charles Ott*, 1219 top (courtesy National Park Service), 1245, 1265 —Jack E. Boucher, 1219 bottom, 1259 —A. W. Moore, 1220 (courtesy of the United States Department of the Interior) —Lloyd Ingles*, 1221, 1223 —Stephen Collins*, 1224 —George Porter*, 1227, 1269 —Arthur W. Ambler*, 1229 —Karl H. Maslowski*, 1230 top —Michael H. Bevans, 1232, 1354, 1355, 1356, 1357, 1359, 1360 —Roland C. Clement, 1233, 1343, 1344, 1365 —John K. Terres, 1242, 1319, 1353, 1362 top and bottom, 1372, 1373, 1376, 1377 top, 1379 top and bottom —W. H. Nicholson, 1243 top and bottom —American Museum of Natural History, 1247, 1253, 1364 —Hugh M. Halliday*, 1251 —Audubon Photo-file Service*, 1255 —Robert Jackowitz, 1257, 1262 —Roy Kligfield, 1272 —Grant Haist*, 1274 75 —Paul A. Moore, 1277 (courtesy of Tennessee Conservation Department) —William H. Sager*, 1279 left —Paul Zahl*, 1279 right top —K. D. Swan, 1279 bottom (courtesy of United States Forest Service) —State of Maine, 1282 —Byron Ashbaugh, 1289, 1290, 1291, 1292 top and bottom, 1293, 1296 top and bottom, 1297 —Edwin Way Teale, 1305, 1307 —Sally Tate, 1309 —Charles E. Mohr*, 1314 —H. W. Kitchen*, 1315 top and bottom, 1316, 1321 —Dur Morton*, 1325 —Lena Scott Harris*, 1333 —Alfred M. Bailey*, 1337 —Territorial Board of Agriculture and Forestry, Hawaii, 1338 —Louis Agassiz Fuertes, 1341 —Allan Brooks, 1342 —Audubon's Elephant Folio, 1347, 1349 —Alfred O. Gross*, 1367 top —George Komorowski*, 1367 bottom —E. O. Mellinger, 1369 (courtesy United States Fish and Wildlife Service) —A. C. Littlejohns, 1371 —G. A. Grant, 1386 (courtesy of National Park Service) —Leonard Lee Rue, III*, 1389 top —F. E. Westlake, 1389 bottom —Olin S. Pettingill, Jr.*, 1390 —W. V. Crick*, 1391 —Lewis Kirk*, 1392

*Photographs from Photo-Film Department of National Audubon Society

Tree oysters cling to the roots of trees in a lagoon in Baja California

MOLLUSK
The Creature in the Shell

Collecting the shells of snails and of other mollusks is one of the most popular of all hobbies, and one that many a person begins as a child and continues throughout his lifetime. Little wonder that this is the case. The variety of shells to be found is almost endless, the beauty of many is jewel-like and behind each kind of shell is an interesting chapter in the vast story of the animal kingdom. Science has placed such animals with shells in one particular group, or phylum (though there are a few included in the phylum which have no shells). This phylum is the Mollusca, a name meaning *soft-bodied,* and its members are popularly known as *mollusks.* The variety of mollusks is tremendous; more than 70,000 species are known. And each of the animal shell-manufacturers creates its own special shape and markings so that a mollusk may be identified by its shell alone. Small wonder a study of shells can provide a lifetime of interest.

Univalves and Bivalves

As we start to look over the great variety of shelled animals, we soon notice that there are two distinct types: Some have double shells while the shells of others are a single unit. Those with the single shell (snails for example) are called *univalves* (one valve); the others are *bivalves* (two valves). Probably the most widely known of the univalves is the snail (*see under Snail*); oysters and clams are easily recognized bivalves (*See Bivalve*). However, to encompass the entire Molluscan phylum and break it into its different classes of close relatives, we need to remember these five: Amphineura (chitons, etc), Scaphopoda (the tooth shells), Pelecypoda (clams, oysters, etc), Gastropoda (snails, cowries etc.) and Cephalopoda (squids, octopi, nautilus, etc.). It may be difficult for a nonscientist to understand why the cephalopodes (*see Cephalopod*) are included in the Mollusca phylum, for most of them do not have an external shell—a feature so characteristic of mollusks. Zoologists who carefully studied their internal structure decided they belonged together. Actually there are varying degrees of shell structure in most cephalopods, from the beautiful covering of the nautilus to the horny plate buried under the mantle of a squid.

Slow but Sure

Mollusks that are the delight of shell collectors, are the snails. Often they are adopted as pets and share an aquarium with goldfishes or are given a home of their own (*See under Aquarium*). As one walks over the aquarium's glass surfaces, it provides excellent views of its soft body. The body varies (as does the shell) with the species, but all snails, as do most mollusks, possess the distinguishing feature called a mantle—a fold of skin enclosing much of the body. A snail has a distinct head (with one or two pairs of tentacles) and a soft, flat mass behind the head which is called the foot. (These two features are not covered by the mantle.) By contracting and expanding its foot, the animal is able to creep about very efficiently. Some species of snails get their oxygen by means of gills; others have lunglike structures.

As a rule it is not possible to have a really friendly relationship with a snail —pet though it may be. On being picked up, the little creature immediately retreats into its shell and resists all invitations to "come on out." However a woman once overcame this behavior pattern with remarkable success. She had picked up a pretty tree snail in Florida and, with great patience, coaxed it to eat from her fingers. Eventually it became tame enough to come out of its shell when she made a sharp, clicking sound—food or no food. It would walk up her arm, and perch on her shoulder, and seemed to enjoy evening excursions into the garden while so situated, leaving her now and then for a short climb up a tree trunk.

Though some snails, like the tree snail, live on land, the greatest number of them are ocean dwellers. Some kinds also live in fresh water—rivers, streams, ponds, and lakes—all of which have their own particular species. However, a number of freshwater snails of the temperate regions resemble certain land species so closely that only a specialist can tell which is which. The food of snails is found in a variety of ways. Certain kinds scrape algae off rocks, using a rasplike structure, called the radula, which is on the underside of the foot. Other snails are flesh-eaters, often preying on the bivalves such as clams and oysters. In this activity they bore a tiny hole in the shell of a victim, then suck out the fleshy body. Most freshwater and land snails feed on both fresh and decayed plant matter.

For a brief time after the young hatch they are without protective covering; actually they are in a larval stage. Soon a variety of developments take place, including the reshaping of the body: The digestive tube bends downward and forward until it lies near the mouth; the head and foot remain stationary while the mass behind the foot is rotated until the anus and the mantle cavity that surrounds it are lying back of the head. As the organs on one side of the body fail to develop, the body mass and the mantle become spirally coiled. Within the mantle are many small glands, located along the outer edge, which produce material—mostly calcium carbonate—to form the shell. This also becomes spirally coiled. Two years are needed for a snail to obtain its full growth. The size and shape of a snail shell varies with the species of snail. Some are flattened; others have a distinct spiral coil. Land snails are quite fragile and more or less thin-shelled in comparison with sea snails.

Many people are primarily interested in the snail as a table delicacy. It was first used as a food in Europe, but a number of *Helix pomatia,* the edible snail, were imported into the United States where they flourished in regions about New Orleans, and now snails are enjoyed by gourmets in many areas of the United States.

Those other famed gastropods, the cowries, are more noted for their shells than are the snails. Among the more than two hundred species, innumerable shells are produced that may be considered works of art, and they are prized by collectors and much used as ornaments.

If one happened upon a cowry when it was "up and doing," one would not see much of its attractive shell, however. With the cowries, when the little animal is crawling, the mantle is expanded on each side, forming lobes that meet over the back of the shell. Usually a line of paler color along the back shows where the mantle lobes meet.

Warfare at the Seashore

Few scenes can give such a feeling of peace and calm as a seashore when the tide is out and there is no movement of wind or waves. Yet in such a setting many a battle may be taking place as one small creature vies with another in the struggle for existence. As has already been mentioned, snails often prey on oysters and clams, boring through the shells to reach the soft bodies. Another enemy of oysters and clams is the mussel; and aside from some mollusks destroying other mollusks, starfishes and crabs are frequent sources of danger. A starfish can wrap its "arms" about a bivalve and pull the shell apart—and the mollusk is completely defenseless. Big crabs can crush many mollusks in their strong pincers. Out from the shore, large fishes, such as sharks, devour mollusks, shells and all, in enormous quantities. Other

Rock snails scour barnacle-covered rocks for green algae. They belong to the molluscan class Gastropoda

Freshwater clam

mollusks that become exposed at low tide are attacked from the air by gulls; the birds carry them high into the air, then drop them on rocks below until their shells break. In areas where walruses live, bivalves have another kind of enemy in these big mammals that dig them out of the mud with their long tusks.

The Ways of a Clam

Clams and oysters may seem to resemble each other very closely, but they differ in a number of ways. Clams live in widely varied localities, and they vary according to their environments.

A truly spectacular saltwater clam is the giant *Tridacna gigas*, a native of South Pacific waters. This enormous mollusk does not try to hide in the ocean floor, but establishes itself in a coral reef, and soon the reef is growing around it. The reef furnishes good protection, and only the outer edges of the clam's shell must be kept free so that the animal can function. Many times the shells grow to a length of three feet and more, and they may weigh several hundred pounds. As a result the *Tridacna* is a real source of danger to divers. A man swimming under water in search of a pearl oyster may not notice the clam's gaping shells among the coral, and should his arm or leg touch the sensitive mantle, the great shells snap shut, possibly imprisoning the diver's limb.

Although freshwater clams can "walk" through sand or mud, they usually do little traveling in the course of a lifetime. When one does want to move, it extends its "foot" into the sand; the tip then swells, acting as an anchor. Next, the muscles of the foot contract, drawing the clam's body forward. However, this mollusk spends most of its life in a certain spot, with its shell slightly agape and with openings for water currents protruding. Water is drawn in, is drained of minute food organisms, and expelled.

The Oyster

An oyster has such a small foot that it cannot readily be seen. From a very early stage of its life this mollusk stays in a fixed position; hence it is helpless before shifting sands and drifting mud which may cover and smother it. And such a happening is only one of the hazards that may result in its destruction. As a result, because of the enormous popularity of oysters as a food, people have taken over the "planting" and raising of the bivalves in suitable localities. The oyster industry employs thousands of persons and is a multi-million-dollar-a-year operation.

In one season a single female oyster may lay millions of eggs. These are merely discharged into the water, and though they are very tiny, the vast number cause the water to look cloudy. The male oysters discharge their sperm into the water also, and when a sperm cell encounters an egg cell, they may join together. The fertilized egg then develops into a tiny larva which bears little hairlike *cilia* by means of which it can swim. The free-swimming larvae go to the surface of the water where they remain for about three weeks. Meanwhile each larva starts to secrete a shell. Soon it is completely encased in a hard covering, but at this point it is only a fraction of an inch in diameter. It is now called a *spat* by oystermen. After its short, roving life, a spat drops to the sea bottom and becomes attached to some solid object by its left valve. There it remains for the rest of its life, each year adding onto its shell "house," making it larger and thicker.

During the period when oyster larvae are swimming or floating, they are eaten in vast numbers by fishes. And they are swept out to sea by storms. A successful technique used by oystermen to cultivate their oyster beds is to locate shallow bays where the surface of the water is well populated with larvae. Into the bottom of such a bay they dump old shells, bricks, tile, brush, and all sorts of junk metal so that when the spat descend, ready to anchor themselves, there is no shortage of suitable "parking spaces." Later the oystermen collect their materials, to which oyster young are now attached, and relocate them in favorable areas—that is, where there are no strong currents or sewage, and where there is a hard mud bottom.

The hard mud is not apt to shift, and on it are likely to be an abundance of marine plants. The smallest of plants and tiny animals that feed on the marine plants all provide natural food for the

Oyster

oysters. The oystermen keep a watch for enemies such as starfishes, destroying them when possible. After about four years they harvest their crop of bivalves.

In contrast to their fame as food products, oysters also have a glamorous reputation as producers of pearls. Other bivalves sometimes create these gems, which are made of the same substance called nacre that lines their shell, but it is the oyster—and particularly the pearl oyster, the *Pteriidae*—that is most famed for its pearls. A pearl may be made when a grain of sand gets between the animal and its shell. Because this is irritating to the soft body, the oyster coats it with the lustrous nacre. Extremely valuable pearls are thought to be formed by a little worm parasite getting into an oyster and forming a cyst in the mouth. The cyst then becomes the center of a beautifully spherical pearl. It is estimated that about a thousand pearl oysters are opened before one good pearl is found.

"The Ship of Pearl"

The sea mollusk called the chambered nautilus, *Nautilus pompilius*, has in thought been related to pearls for many years, but not because it produces them. It was made famous by Oliver Wendell Holmes' poem, "The Chambered Nautilus." He wrote, "This is the ship of pearl," and his analogy is easy to appreciate if we see one of the handsome shells: the entire thickness, beneath a thin colored surface, is a beautiful iridescent mother-of-pearl. Few people have seen the chambered nautilus in its natural habitat which is the rather deep waters of the Pacific and Indian oceans. We know, however, that this nautilus constructs a whole series of "chambers." As it outgrows one, it moves forward, building a new, larger enclosure. Thus one chamber follows another, creating a coiled and curved structure, somewhat like a giant snail shell. The body of the nautilus may be six or seven inches long, and on its head are about ninety

tentacles arranged around the mouth. As the animal is always at the opening of its last-built chamber, these tenacles can reach out to grasp food from the water; they also assist the nautilus in traveling along the ocean bottom.

Another nautilus is the argonaut, or "paper," nautilus—"paper" referring to the extreme thinness of its shell when dry. The name argonaut was suggested by the famous ship of mythology, for this mollusk often may be seen scudding over the water's surface, suggesting a very tiny sailboat. Actually its motion is not caused by sailing but by jets of water that it expels with great force. It is only the female that may be seen by keen-eyed travelers, for the "shell" is actually a loose egg case; it does not cover the body of the animal and it can be dropped off at will. In the species seen most commonly in Atlantic waters, *Argonauta argo*, the female is about eight inches long and her shell is about the same length. The male is a mere inch in length; he suggests a miniature squid or octopus.

The argonaut, therefore, does not really merit being grouped with "creatures in their shells," but it *is* a mollusk and the female does produce a shell—and it is an interesting reminder of the wide variety of animals, from giant squids to tiny snails, that belong to the phylum Mollusca.　　　　—D.E.S.

Recommended Reading

Animals Without Backbones—Ralph Buchsbaum. The University of Chicago Press. Chicago

A Field Guide to Shells of Our Atlantic and Gulf Coasts: A Field Guide to Shells of the Pacific Coast and Hawaii—Percy A. Morris. Houghton Mifflin Company, Boston, Mass.

The Lower Animals: Living Invertebrates of the World— Ralph Buchsbaum and Lorus J. Milne. Doubleday & Company, Inc., Garden City, New York

My Hobby is Collecting Sea Shells and Coral—Ruth H. Dudley. Childrens Press, Chicago.

Sea Treasure—Kathleen Yerger Johnstone. Houghton Mifflin Company, Boston.

Sea Shells of the World: A Guide to the Better Known Species—R. Tucker Abbott and Herbert S. Zim. Golden Press, New York.

MONKEY
Facts About Some American Monkeys

Compared with their Old World relatives, the monkeys of the tropical forests of Central and South America are fairly small. They have more teeth than the Old World monkeys, are lightly built, and most of them have a prehensile, or grasping, tail.

The night monkey, or douroucouli, (*Aotus* spp.) is the only tropical American monkey that is active at night. It is small, only a little larger than a gray squirrel; the tail is as long as, or longer than, its body. It feeds mainly on fruit, tender leaves, the stems of plants, and on insects.

The squirrel monkey, or squirrel marmoset (*Saimiri*) is 10 to 15 inches long, with a tail about 14 to 18 inches long. There are half a dozen species of squirrel monkeys that inhabit the tropics from Costa Rica southward to Brazil and Bolivia. They are active in the daytime and prefer scrubby timber and underbrush to the dense forest. They eat insects, spiders, fruits, and small birds.

The howler monkey (*Alouatta*), of which there are at least six or eight species from Mexico southward, is the largest of all American monkeys. It is 22 to 36 inches long, with a prehensile tail 23 to 26 inches long. Adult males often have heavy beards that hide the large lower jaw and throat, which encloses the hyoid bone. This bone is a greatly enlarged sounding box that enables them to make their remarkably loud cries.

There are possibly a dozen species of capuchin (*Cebus*) monkeys in tropical America. These are the monkeys that accompanied the sidewalk organ-grinders of the last century, and early in this one, in cities of the United States. The best known and most attractive of these is the white-throated capuchin, *Cebus capucinus*.

Spider monkeys (*Ateles*) are 16 to 24 inches long, with a tail 21 to 30 inches in length. The very long tail is prehensile, and is used by them as an extra arm or an extra leg. Their arms, legs, hands, feet, and bodies are very slender, and they are strictly tree dwellers, rarely descending to the ground as some monkeys do. They are second only to the Old World gibbons in their agility in trees.
—J.K.T.

The Monkeys of Barro Colorado

The douroucoulis are one of four kinds of monkeys living on Barro Colorado Island, Panama Canal Zone. The tall almendro trees are but one of many forest giants that with smaller trees, palms, shrubs, tree ferns, and bromeliads, orchids, and other epiphytes, make up the tropical evergreen forest that except for a clearing of perhaps six acres, covers the island.

Barro Colorado Island was set aside by the United States Congress in 1923 as a tropical research laboratory. Before the canal was built, it was a forested hill beside whose red cliffs the pirate Henry Morgan camped on his cross-country march to the ill-fated city of Old Panama. When the waters of the mighty Chagres River were impounded to form Gatun Lake in the building of the canal, the hilltop became an island of nearly six square miles.

To this island, which is a part of the great Smithsonian Institution, scientists travel from all over the world to study the plants and animals that live there. They have published many books, popular articles, and scientific papers of their studies. Yet the forests of Barro Colorado still contain many unsolved scientific problems. Each new study suggests others. Perhaps the surface is hardly scratched. For example, little is known about the life history of the Canal Zone douroucouli, or night monkey.

The douroucouli is about the size of a tree squirrel. It has a soft gray coat and a nonprehensile tail that terminates in a small brush. Like many other nocturnal animals its big, solemn, black eyes appear far too large for its small size. Douroucoulis are said to make ideal pets, especially for people who must spend the daytime working away from home. At night it is alert, ready to play, and is an affectionate and interesting companion. The species is not believed to travel in troops like the capuchin and howler monkeys.

Unlike the tropical trails along which the humans walk, the tree trails of the monkeys are not cut by a machete. To the monkeys the markers must be clear, for each day they seem to follow along the same branches, climb up the same long swinging lianas, and jump from the same trees. The soft gray-and-brown-flecked coats and bright eyes of the squirrel monkeys give them a deceptively friendly, innocent look.

In the forest, the squirrel monkeys chatter to each other while scurrying through the trees and often call in high-pitched, squeaky tones. From a distance, they resemble squirrels. They are reported to travel in small bands. Although they make the tree trails their own, they do not travel them with the grace of the capuchin monkeys. Here again they are more like squirrels. With the exception of the great toe, their toes are claw-tipped. This is useful in certain types of climbing, but does not give the animal the purchase upon a limb so necessary for truly arboreal life.

Scientists who have studied squirrel monkeys report that they eat a variety of foods. They like star apples, wild figs, seeds, and blossoms. Probably they eat very little meat, except possibly insects. Captive animals liked grasshoppers and cooked meat but showed no interest in raw meat that was offered them on Barro Colorado. These squirrel monkeys do not appear to be nearly as numerous as the capuchin and howler monkeys. Perhaps they prefer to live in small trees at the edge of clearings and to shun the deep forest.

On Barro Colorado there is plenty of deep forest, hanging lianas, and shrubby tangles. From such a habitat as this, one hears each morning the roarlike barks of the howler monkeys giving blatant welcome to the new day. From a distance the loud reverberating voice of *Mono negro*, or *caraya*, as the natives call the howler monkey, is extremely impressive. When one is standing below the tree in which a clan is resting, the deep growls, which in unison become a loud roar, are wild and terrifying. Yet there is something about a howler's face, seen at close range, that is very appealing in spite of its large size. Their numbers on the island appear to have decreased in the past few decades. Perhaps the monkey yellow fever, which swept north from South America into Panama, Costa Rica, and Nicaragua, took its toll among the Barro Colorado howler clans as it did elsewhere. But it is difficult to ascertain. When death comes to a tropical forest dweller, there are many other animals ready to pick its bones.

When observed in the dense woods, howlers are usually high in the largest trees. The monkeys do not move away when they realize that they are being watched, but jump up and down shaking the limbs and often breaking and dropping small branches toward the observer.

Howler monkeys travel through the trees slowly and cautiously. Unlike the capuchins, they never make long jumps, but progress carefully from the terminal branches of one tree to the terminal branches of the next. When necessary the prehensile tail is used as an anchor to keep the animal from falling off the branch on which it is sleeping or to catch a branch or vine in case of a fall. Often the band is led by a large male in his prime. The young males and females follow. Mothers carrying their babies come last. When the young are very small their mothers carry them on their breasts; as they grow older they learn to ride "pick-a-back."

In the Barro Colorado forest there is ample food. The crop of almendro nuts in February is excellent. There are many figs and other fruits and plenty of young, sweet leaf buds. All of these are eaten by

A red howler monkey

Spider monkey

howler monkeys. This species is largely free of enemies on the island. Its large size and tree-dwelling habits save it from ground-dwelling predators large enough to do it damage, although the young may be killed by ocelots. There, howler monkeys, as elsewhere, are probably heavily infected with botflies. Probably man is the howler's greatest enemy, but no man hunts on this island sanctuary.

Even though the numbers of howler monkeys have diminished, there is no more characteristic sound on the island than the deep voice of *Mono negro*. It is often heard in the quiet of dawn or in the still calm before a tropical storm breaks into a torrent of rain.

The capuchin monkeys are the comedians of the forest. They travel through the trees with gay abandon, jumping carelessly from one tree to the next. To the onlooker they seem to be playing a game of tag or follow-the-leader. Sometimes they break off dead twigs and throw them into the water. It seems that they like to hear them splash. The large iguanas that habitually rest in the trees jump with great splashes into the water when the monkeys get within reach of them.

When the deep-throated, gobletlike blossoms of the balsa tree bloom, the capuchin monkeys make early morning and late evening trips to the trees. Climbing out on the limbs, they squat beside the blossoms. They take the flower in both hands and lift it to their mouths. Sometimes they lean over and bury their faces in the pale yellow blossom. Perhaps they drink the water that has accumulated in the cup, or eat the pollen and the insects that may be caught there. The capuchins are more carnivorous than the other island monkeys. They like insects, bird's eggs and young birds, small arboreal rodents, and possibly bats. The bulk of their food is vegetable including figs, star apples, manzabis, tree leaves, and nuts.

The native boys on Barro Colorado call the white-faced capuchin monkeys *Mono cara blanca*. On the mainland the species is rare because the natives hunt them for food or sell them as pets. On Barro Colorado, capuchins are numerous. Unlike the howlers, which travel comparatively short distances, the capuchins seem to move widely over the island. They have set routes over which bands of 15 to 25 scatter out for a hundred yards or more, and run easily over branches or climb swinging lianas.

A visitor from the North, familiar with the unhappy faces of zoo monkeys is quite unprepared for the beauty and charm of these wild primates in the jungle. There the destructive and selfish interests of man do not threaten their safety, and they move with confidence and freedom over the serpentine lianas or through the spreading broad-leaved trees that make up the forest arterials of their tree trails.   —E.I.

MONKEY FLOWER
Salmon Bush Monkey Flower
Other Common Names—None
Scientific Name—*Mimulus longiflorus*
Family—Scrophulariaceae (figwort family)
Range—Southern California from Kern and San Luis Obispo counties to northern Baja California
Habitat—Rocky canyons and chaparral Upper Sonoran Zone
Time of Blooming—March to July

The monkey flower is most generous with its gift of color, and in almost any section of the state some one of the more than forty species will be found in bloom—usually between April and October. Some are definite shrubs but the majority are herbs (*Mimulus*). The wide grinning corolla inspired the name monkey flower—*Mimulus,* from the Latin *mimus,* a comic actor.

The flowers are very gay as they sway from canyon walls, along roadsides, from stream banks, and even from shallow creeks. The colors include straw, salmon, flame red, brick-red, red-brown with outline of clear yellow on each petal, pink, deep and pale yellow, mahogany, crimson, scarlet, purple—the gamut of strong colors. An exquisite one, scarlet monkey flower, *Mimulus cardinalis,* haunts mountain streams, the inside of the very large flowers being scarlet and the outside a satiny yellow, all made more intense by the large, roundish leaves. The different species are as varied in size as in color, some being no more than three inches tall, others reaching a height of four feet.

MONOCOTYLEDON

The flowering plants (angiosperms) are divided into two groups, of which the monocotyledons, or monocots, are one. These are the plants that have seeds possessing only one seed leaf, or cotyledon. Those plants whose seeds have two cotyledons are the dicotyledons, or dicots.

Monocotyledons have parallel veining in the leaves, scattered vascular bundles in the stems, and floral parts in multiples of three. They comprise the grasses, lilies, pondweeds, cattails, sedges, rushes, irises, pineapples, bananas, skunk cabbages, duckweeds, orchids, and one family of treelike plants, the palms.

—G.B.S.

Gamagrass has parallel-veined leaves that are characteristic of most monocots

MOOSE
Other Common Names—None
Scientific Name—*Alces alces*
Family—Cervidae (deer family)
Order—Artiodactyla
Size—Male: body length, 8 to 10 feet; height at shoulder, 5½ to 7½ feet; weight, 900 to 1,400 pounds, sometimes up to 1,800 pounds. Female slightly smaller
Range—Alaska, Canada (except northeastern Mackenzie and northwestern Keewatin, southeastern Alberta and southern Saskatchewan, northern Quebec and Franklin Territory). In United States, the interior mountains of western North America, and from eastern North Dakota across northern portions of the northeastern states, all of New England, south to Pennsylvania

Moose are the largest deer in the world and are characteristic of the spruce forests, swamps, and shallow lakes of the North. A mature bull may weigh over half a ton and carry a six-foot span of antlers, but he can move through dense thickets without a sound.

Life Story of the Moose

Travelers in the forested areas of northern North America may occasionally see a bull moose standing by the roadside, his great head and antlers lifted as though to challenge their right to be there. And, if they look away for a moment, then look back, they may be startled that in spite of its size and awkward appearance it has vanished into the brush without a sound.

The appearance of the bull moose is dominated by his antlers, which are flat and broad, spreading widely, with up-curved sweeping sections and many points, or tines, along the edges. They may be 6 feet wide; a record set of antlers taken in Alaska was 78 inches wide, had 34 points, and weighed 85 pounds, exclusive of the skull.

The bull moose's deep-chested body seems awkwardly balanced on his thin, knobby, 4½-foot long legs. His tail is very short and flat. His big head is carried forward and down, from the height of his shoulder hump, on a short neck. His muzzle is long and inflated with an overhanging upper lip that may be moved back and forth. His ears are large and independently mobile. Hanging below his throat is a flap of skin and hair called the bell, which may be 3 feet long but is usually no longer than about 12 to 18 inches. His furry coat is an inch thick and is a dark gray-brown to almost black, but lighter-colored on his muzzle and legs.

The rutting season of the moose is from September until November, but may continue into December if the weather remains unusually warm. During this time the bull will charge just about anything of size that he sees, perhaps under the impression that it is a rival, perhaps out of plain bad temper. Unlike the elk and caribou, he does not collect a harem but takes one mate for a week or ten days, and then goes off to seek another.

His mating bellow sounds something like a diesel horn and may be heard as far. Two bull moose fighting will pant, grunt, and push furiously, antler to antler. With lowered heads, they appraise each other. Suddenly the great antlers clash together and the fight is on, accompanied by terrible roars and an ever-present whine or humming sound. The ground is torn up, trees snapped off, and the brush flattened over a large area, for the battle arena moves to a new location when one or the other runs for a hundred yards or so, seemingly to catch his breath before renewing the struggle.

One contestant may give up and run away. Rarely, one moose may kill another or they may lock antlers and perish together. Somewhere nearby a cow moose awaits the outcome of the fight between the rivals.

The antlerless cow is a three-quarter-size edition of the bull, and with a smaller, less bearded bell. Her calf is a still smaller replica of herself, with the bell but without the shoulder hump and the long upper lip. Its legs are relatively longer and thinner and its coat is light-colored with a dark muzzle and marks over the eyes.

The bull moose's handsome antlers, like those of all the deer family are shed each year. The moose drops his in early spring, and they reappear in May as nobs covered with soft, fuzzy skin. All summer as they grow to full size they are covered by this velvet. In late summer the skin covering dries and is rubbed off against a tree trunk, to expose the white of the bone of which the antlers are composed. Later they darken from exposure and remain unchanged until the resorption of the bone at their base causes them to drop off at the end of the winter.

With the young bull moose, the antlers increase from spikes in a yearling to a

An adult moose stands from 5 to 7 feet or more at the shoulder

maximum size with many edging tines in a mature bull of about twelve years, at which time the bell also reaches its greatest development. As the animal ages, the antlers grow smaller and have fewer tines with each year, and the bell diminishes until it is a mere flap of skin in a very old bull.

In May or June the cow seeks a secluded spot—a small island is a favorite—and there bears her calf or calves. Twins are quite common and triplets occur rarely. They are skinny and comical-looking and are about 32 inches tall. They have attenuated, shaky legs, and stay very close to the mother. Much grown, they are still with her when she mates again in the fall. The following spring, the calf is about five feet tall, and when the birth of its successor is imminent, the cow drives the yearling away.

Moose live only in densely forested areas, usually near shallow lakes or swamps. During the winter they may gather in small bands, made up of a bull or two, several cows, and their accompanying calves. These groups may winter in thick swamps, browsing over nearby hills. When the snow becomes very deep in the swamp and their long legs cannot carry them easily through it, they make *yards* by moving about continually and packing down the snow. With the coming of spring and summer, the groups have broken up—the cows travel with their calves, and the lone females and lone bulls travel their solitary ways through the woods, grazing and chewing their cuds.

As the moose have no upper incisors or canine teeth, they must scoop their food upward instead of biting it off. They feed on a wide variety of plants and are helped by their height and extraordinary reach.

They graze with no difficulty on shrubs such as alder and the various berries, jewelweed and similar tall plants, and ferns. Their long legs, short necks, and deep chests prevent them from reaching the ground to feed. If they have a taste for moss or low-growing lichens, they kneel and move slowly ahead, neatly cropping the plants as they go. The leaves of aspen, birch, maple, cherry, and other deciduous trees are stripped easily to a height of 9 or 10 feet and if the moose wants more, it may nudge the branches down with its muzzle and eat leaves that grow 20 feet up. If the tree is small—perhaps up to three inches in diameter—the moose may simply straddle it with its front legs and break it down. The moose is fond of the upper bark of the aspen and may break down these small trees in the winter and spring, or hunt for windfalls. Its winter food is mainly fir and the buds and twigs of the trees and shrubs that it eats in the warmer months. And it is so fond of ground juniper, a type of yew often very appropriately called "shintangle," that it may graze it to virtual extermination.

For the same reason, water lilies and other succulent water-growing plants may disappear in an area where moose are plentiful. The animal prefers to wade into water three or four feet deep, duck its head under the surface, and come up with a whole plant. It is said to be able to keep its head submerged as long as two minutes.

The moose enters the water in spring to escape from the torture of black fly bites and may sometimes wallow in mud to further protect itself. But it enjoys licking mud all through the year and may even dig through snow and ice to reach it. It has no fear of the deep ooze of swamps and will plow steadily through the muck with occasional pauses to rest. It is also a strong swimmer and does not hesitate to cross miles of water, even in bitter cold. A cow may take her calf with her on a summer swim and, if it tires, it may rest its head on her body or throw a leg over her neck and she will tow its weight with ease.

On the whole, the moose does not make unprovoked attacks on people. A cow may defend her calf, but is more likely to withdraw with it if startled. The bull, except during the rut, seems to be more curious than alarmed or angry if approached within a reasonable distance. If seriously bothered, bulls may chase people into trees and keep them there for hours. Sometimes they will patrol the door of a cabin so that the occupant is a prisoner.   —H.H.

The largest deer in North America, mature moose bulls may weigh 900 to 1,400 or even 1,800 pounds

Female mosquitos feed on blood, puncturing the skin with a stiletto-like beak

MOSQUITO
Common House Mosquito
Other Common Names — None
Scientific Name — *Culex pipiens*
Family — Culicidae (mosquitoes)
Order — Diptera
Size — Length, one-fourth to one-half inch
Range — Worldwide

The fact that a mosquito, besides being a mosquito, is a fly may surprise many people. While becoming aware of it will surely not cause them to feel any more kindly toward this annoying insect, it is worth noting that mosquitoes belong to an enormous group in the animal kingdom — the order Diptera — which, though it has many "villains," is judged, on the whole, to be beneficial to mankind (*See also under Fly*).

The mosquito is a fly that can ruin enjoyment of the out-of-doors by the irritating itching its bite produces. Some can also spread such life-draining plagues as yellow fever, malaria, and encephalitis (*See Encephalitis*).

Because they can be a major menace to health as well as being a nuisance, it is of special importance to know why mosquitoes flourish so successfully, and laymen as well as scientists should gain an understanding of their life histories. Does this seem a fairly simple task? It might be if there were just one kind of mosquito, but the fact is about 2,000 species are known to exist. More than 500 species are found in South America

alone and more than 200 species flourish in North America. Their habits differ widely, although there are certain characteristics common to all. One of these is the necessity for the larvae to develop in water. Without watery "nurseries" the mosquito population would soon vanish. However, there is wide variation in the length of time needed for a larval mosquito to grow into adulthood. Some species that breed in rain pools pass from egg to adult in three or four days. Others, breeding in locations of greater permanence such as water lying within old tree trunks, may take months to go through the same process.

Although mosquito breeding is so concerned with water, the larvae are not to be found on open lakes or swift-running streams. They may, however, make use of the edges where vegetation protects them or of quiet spots that are furnished by such natural barriers as boulders and gravel bars. As a rule they hang from the film that covers the surface of quiet water. All kinds but the Anopheles, *Anopheles quadrimaculatus,* take in air by means of a tube at the tail end of the body. For this reason, oil poured on water is a good method of controlling mosquito development. The little tubes cannot pierce the oil covering. In tropical forests where rain accumulates in all sorts of odd places, there seems to be a special species of mosquito for almost every type of pool. Larvae are popularly known as *wrigglers* because of their manner of moving.

A mosquito larva nourishes itself with tiny plant and animal life such as algae and protozoa; but once the adult emerges, the diet changes. The males feed on plant juices and so do the females to some extent. But the females of most species have another important kind of food—blood. Many questions arise concerning this item of diet: Is it absolutely necessary to mosquitoes that they consume blood? Must it be human blood? Why does their bite cause swelling and itching?

The blood consumption has much to do with egg production. Females, with the exception of some species, must feed at least once on the blood of man or beast before their eggs can develop properly. Some authorities consider that blood is to the mosquito what minerals and vitamins are to a person, keeping it healthy and strong. Human blood is not necessarily best for the purpose; other mammals and birds may give sustenance that is more potent. Strangely enough, the common house mosquito, *Culex pipiens*, which gives us so much discomfort with its biting is among the few species which can develop eggs without a blood meal. The reason a bite causes swelling and itching is that the mosquito's beak carries on it some saliva from the mouth

and this, inserted into the flesh, causes an unpleasant reaction. It may also carry *viruses* if the insect has recently bitten a "carrier" of disease.

After a female mosquito has had her fill of blood, she devotes herself to digesting the meal. The time required may be from two days to a week, depending on the prevailing temperatures and on the kind of mosquito. The number of eggs produced also depend on the kind of mosquito as well as on the amount and kind of blood she has consumed; it may vary from 100 to 400.

The house mosquitoes lay their eggs chiefly during May and June. Sitting on the water film of the surface of a puddle, the female deposits one egg after another until all are laid. She then manipulates them with her hind legs into a small "raft," held together by a sticky substance.

The egg-laying performance of the Anopheles is lively in contrast with that of *Culex pipiens*, the house mosquito, for the female carries on a kind of dance several inches above the water's surface, dropping her eggs as she bobs up and down. Mosquito eggs which land on dry soil may hatch eventually if rains or melting snow provide the moisture they need.

It is only the busy female mosquito

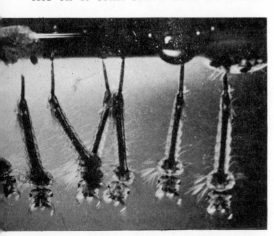

Mosquito larvae breath through tubes that extend to the surface of the water under which they develop

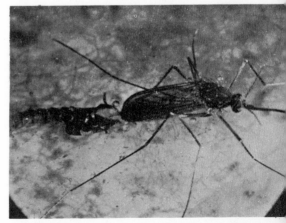

A female mosquito emerges from her pupal case that she leaves behind her on the water's surface

Mosquitos are flies and have a single pair of functional wings

that "sings" or "hums" —a noise made by vibrating the thin scales that lie across her breathing pores. Males and females may be distinguished by a close look at their antennae: those of the male are conspicuous and featherlike while those of the female are more simple

A popular point of interest about the mosquito is: How long does one live as an adult "biting" insect? Again the answer is not simple for there are many variations to the life span. Apparently some live for only a few days but the Anopheles, it is known, must live for at least a week or two because this much time is needed to incubate the yellow fever or malaria "germs" transmittable from one person to another. Then there are the species both in Europe and in North America that pass the winter in the adult stage, hibernating in sheltered spots and sustained by a last "blood meal" of the fall.

Another popular question is: Why are mosquitoes attracted to some people more than to others? Extensive laboratory tests have revealed that body heat is the factor by which mosquitoes locate their victims, and that the chemical components of the breath exhaled by any individual determines the appeal he will have for the menacing insects. Tests have borne out a theory that mosquitoes are attracted to dark colors rather than to light. —D.E.S.

Recommended Reading

Insects of the Pacific World—C.H. Curran. The Macmillan Company, New York.
1001 Questions Answered About Insects—Alexander B. and Elsie B. Klots. Dodd, Mead & Company, New York.

MOSSES AND LIVERWORTS

The mosses and liverworts are nonvascular (without vessels or ducts), green plants that have stalked sex organs, or *antheridia*. Together they form the phylum Bryophyta which is divided into two classes the Musci (mosses) and the Hepaticae (liverworts). The chief difference between some of the simpler Bryophytes and the more advanced algae (*see Alga*) is in the more complex reproductive structures of the mosses and liverworts. These green plants have primitive stems and leaves, and reproduce by spores in one phase of their life history.

All of the mosses and liverworts are small and usually require study of their parts with a hand lens of at least 10 power magnification. Most of them require considerable and continual moisture in order to grow, but some species have adapted to desert conditions; a few grow either in or under water. Most of them, however, grow on soil, rocks, the bark of trees, or decaying logs in shaded woods and ravines. Mosses are very important to soil-building and help to prevent erosion. By gradually filling lakes and ponds, mosses help transform many small bodies of water into land (*See under Bog*).

A typical moss has a short axis containing a simple circulatory system. Rhizoids, rootlike structures, hold the axis to the ground or other surface. The leaves are arranged spirally on the surface of the axis and consist of a single layer of cells. Male and female sex organs grow at the tip of the axis, or stem, and the male gametes, or sperms, swim through surface moisture to the female cells. These then develop a foot that clamps to the leaf from which grows a seta, or stalk, that extends upward and at the end of which develops a capsule that contains spores that will become new moss plants.

Sphagnum moss is an economically valuable species. It grows in bogs, partly submerged, and its decayed remains are known as peat (*See also under Coal*).

A typical liverwort has a flat leaflike structure at its base. These have small cups on their upper surface in which tiny buds, or *gemmae*, form. From these buds new plants develop asexually. In addition, some of the broad thallose liverworts have small erect stalks that support bottle-shaped structures, or *archegonia*, in which large egg cells develop. Other stalks bear the male reproductive structures, or *antheridia*, in which many free-swimming sperms are produced. These sperms transport themselves through a film of water, supplied by rain or dew, until they reach the neck canal of the female reproductive body. Once inside, they contact the egg cell and a stalk with a spore case at its tip develops. These are scattered by the wind and new liverworts develop from them.   —G.A.B.

Some Common Mosses

The small things of the earth have a delicacy of color and a fine perfection of shape and structure that never fails to arouse one's interest in these smaller forms of life, whether plant or animal. Among the lesser plants of the woods are the mosses; and once interest in these is begun, it can hardly fail to be sustained by their endless variety of forms and adaptations.

When compared with ferns or seed plants, mosses are a primitive kind of plantlife. Their life cycle, however, is very interesting. If one shakes the capsule of a moss plant a fine dust sifts out into the wind. This dust is composed of thousands of exceedingly tiny spores. A spore contains but a single cell, and, because it is so light, it can be wafted on the breeze for great distances. If the spore falls upon moist earth, it will germinate, growing into a long, branching chain of cells called a *protonema*. This protonema, which resembles some of the algae or pond scums in appearance, soon produces buds here and there along its branches. Each bud develops into a green moss plant.

The protonema branches so widely and so many plants arise from the buds that mats of mosses thus cover the ground. Eventually, organs bearing egg cells and others bearing sperm cells are produced by the leafy moss plants. Often these organs develop in rosettes at the top of the moss plants, but in a large group of mosses they may be produced along the stem. In wet weather, or under the melting snow in spring, the motile sperm cells swim to the egg cells. The result of the union of these cells is a new plant growing from the top of the leafy shoot.

This new plant is a spore-bearing plant and consists merely of a capsule on top of a long, wiry stalk called a *seta*. The base of the seta is embedded in the top of the stem of the leafy moss plant and absorbs nourishment and water from it. Thus it can be seen that the spore-bearing plant is at least a partial parasite on the leafy plant. Two types of plants, then, alternate in the life cycle of a moss: the spores from the spore-bearing plant giving rise to the leafy moss plants, and

SOME

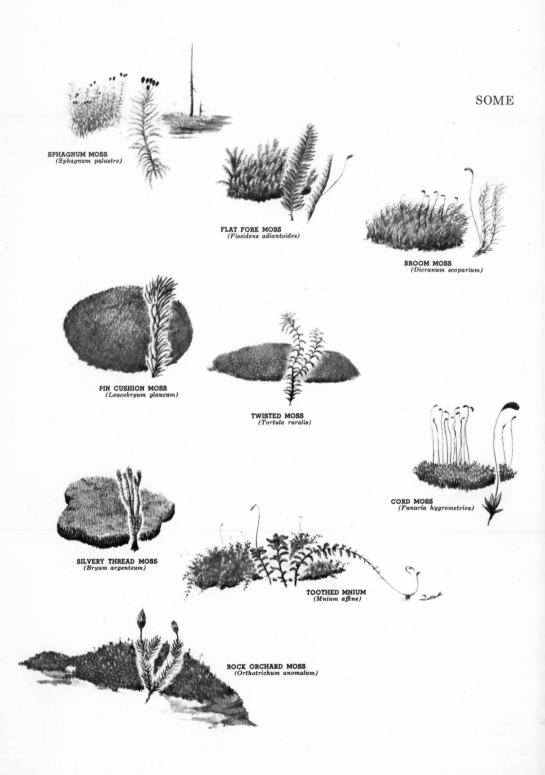

SPHAGNUM MOSS
(Sphagnum palustre)

FLAT FORK MOSS
(Fissidens adiantoides)

BROOM MOSS
(Dicranum scoparium)

PIN CUSHION MOSS
(Leucobryum glaucum)

TWISTED MOSS
(Tortula ruralis)

CORD MOSS
(Funaria hygrometrica)

SILVERY THREAD MOSS
(Bryum argenteum)

TOOTHED MNIUM
(Mnium affine)

ROCK ORCHARD MOSS
(Orthotrichum anomalum)

COMMON MOSSES

TREE MOSS
(Climacium americanum)

WIRE ROCK MOSS
(Hedwigia ciliata)

COMMON FERN MOSS
(Thuidium delicatulum)

PLUME MOSS
(Ptilium crista-castrensis)

MOUNTAIN FERN MOSS
(Hylocomium splendens)

COMMON HAIR-CAP MOSS
(Polytrichum commune)

GRAIN OF WHEAT MOSS
(Diphyscium foliosum)

COMMON WATER MOSS
(Fontinalis dalicarlica)

BEARD MOSS
(Pogonatum pensilvanicum)

the leafy plants producing egg and sperm cells which unite to produce the spore-bearing plant.

Many mosses are difficult to identify unless the spore-bearing plants are present, as the capsules are very distinctive. A hand lens is a very necessary help in identification because the structures of mosses are so tiny. The capsules are cup-shaped (variously modified organs) usually closed by a lid when young. Over this, there may be a cap, or *calyptra,* which is a remnant of the organ that bore the egg cell. It later protects the young spore-bearing plant, but soon disappears. The lid of the capsule drops off when the spores are ripe, exposing a fringe of teeth around the mouth of the capsule. These teeth act as a salt or pepper shaker in distributing the spores in the wind. To assist in this distribution the seta is very elastic and when pushed to one side, springs back, releasing a shower of spores from the capsule. Passing animals, brushing against the plants, sometimes raise clouds of spores at each step. The teeth of the capsule are composed of a substance which absorbs water readily; and in wet weather they close the mouth of the capsule to retain the spores until the weather is more favorable. The teeth may vary in number from 4 (in the common Georgia moss) to 64 and are almost always in multiples of 4.

Where can one find mosses? Of course, the tundras of arctic regions are covered mainly by large swards of mosses and lichens. But in the more temperate regions mosses are also very common although they are not always conspicuous. The soil of old fields, rocks, and soil in moist woods, the trunks of trees, and old rotting logs all are excellent places for hunting mosses. Some species in the tropical forests even grow on the leaves of trees. Like the lichens, however, they do not grow well in the immediate vicinity of large cities; although a few species may be found within the limits even of a city like New York.

Although at first thought mosses may appear to be of little value, their ability to absorb large quantities of water is of great importance in water conservation and flood control. As ground cover they effectively prevent soil erosion. Also, following the lichens on sterile soil and rocks, they pave the way for the growth of higher plants. These find root space in the debris that mosses accumulate; and finally trees are able to grow in the humus thus formed.

The only moss that is of any great

Sphagnum moss is important in the formation of peat

commercial importance is sphagnum. In bogs the sphagnum mosses form the tremendous beds of peat which in Europe are used for fuel. The bogs are drained, blocks of peat cut and dried, and a fuel of low heating value thus obtained. In this country, mainly in the area covered by the glaciers during the Great Ice Age, there are tremendous, almost unused peat resources. Gardeners use the peat to improve the tilth of their soils. Another use of this moss is found in packing flowers and nursery stock. For this purpose the growing moss rather than the peat deposit is used. So great are the absorbent properties of some kinds of sphagnum that in both World Wars they were used for surgical dressings. Up to 200 times its own weight of water may be held by fresh bog sphagnum.

Things to do with Mosses

Learn the common mosses of your region and make a collection of them. There are many valuable studies yet to be made on these plants.

Take field trips and study the different mosses to be found in different habitats.

Experiment with growing mosses in a terrarium. Some kinds grow very well and others do not. In general those growing on soil do better than those found on rotting wood or bark.

Try growing moss spores in chemical gardens or nutrient solutions.

Collect cord moss and alternately moisten and dry the stalk to watch it twist and untwist with changes in the moisture. The stalk contains the same water absorbing substance as the teeth of the capsule.

Study the water absorbing powers of sphagnum mosses. Note how many times its own weight of water your samples will take up.

Keep a record of the different dates on which moss "fruits" or spore-bearing plants become ready to shed spores. Very little of this type of scientific data is available for different parts of the country.
—J.W.T.

Recommended Reading

Check List of Pleurocarpus Mosses of North America — A.J. Grout. The Chicago Natural History Museum, Chicago.
How to Know the Mosses — Henry S. Conrad. William C. Brown, Dubuque, Iowa.
How to Know the Mosses — E.M. Dunham. Mosher Press, Boston.
Illustrated Glossary of Bryological Terms — A.J. Grout. The Chicago Natural History Museum, Chicago.
An Introduction to the Mosses and Lichens — Coauthors, Farida A. Wiley and John W. Thomson, with contributions by Inez Haring. Devin-Adair Company, New York.
Mosses — E.T. Bodenberg. Burgess Publishing Company, Minneapolis, Minnesota.
Moss Flora of North America North of Mexico (3 volumes) — A.J. Grout. The Chicago Natural History Museum, Chicago.
Mosses with a Hand-Lens — A.J. Grout. The Chicago Natural History Museum, Chicago.

MOTH

Moths and butterflies are scaly-winged insects that belong to the order Lepidoptera (*lepis*, scale; and *pteron*, wing). These insects have two pairs of wings that are given their beautiful designs and colors by a covering of minute scales arranged like shingles on a roof. Most moths and butterflies are equipped with sucking-tube mouthparts in the adult stage. All members of the order Lepidoptera have complete metamorphosis, that is, they are hatched from eggs in the form of larvae, or caterpillars, then, rest as pupae before changing into winged adults.

Several characteristics serve to distinguish the moths from the butterflies. Moths fly commonly at night, have stout bodies, some spin cocoons, and their antennae are feathered or threadlike. In addition, they hold their wings flat or folded against their bodies when at rest. Butterflies, on the other hand, fly by day, have slender bodies, never spin true cocoons, and always have club-shaped antennae. The wings of butterflies are held vertically over the body when at rest.

Female moths usually lay eggs in masses, then cover them with scales. The caterpillars have chewing mouthparts and most of them live on vegetation. They pupate in a cocoon and emerge as winged adults. (*See also Butterflies and Moths.*)   —G.B.S.

Silkworm Moths

The giant silkworm moths, (family Saturniidae) are our largest moths. They have stout hairy bodies, beautifully feathered antennae, and large, strong, distinctively colored wings. The female lays three or four hundred eggs, usually in rows or in clusters. Voracious feeders upon the leaves of a great variety of trees and shrubs, the caterpillars grow rapidly, changing their skins at intervals. The full grown larvae spin large silken cocoons in which pupation takes place. The adults have poorly developed mouthparts and do not feed, their one function being to reproduce their kind.

Cecropia Moth
Other Common Names — None
Scientific Name — *Samia cecropia*
Family — Saturniidae (silkworm moths)
Order — Lepidoptera
Size — Length, 1¼ inches; wingspread, 5½ inches
Range — Eastern United States except southern tip of Florida. North to southern Manitoba, Ontario, Quebec, New Brunswick, and Nova Scotia

Cecropia moth

This is the largest and most strikingly colored of our giant silkworm moths. The wings are dusky red or gray-brown with a wide outer margin of lighter color, and a whitish moon-shaped mark on each wing. The head, body, and bases of the forewings are rich red except for white bands. The larva, usually about four inches long, is bluish-green, with yellow, blue, and red tubercles. The large cocoon, made of tough silk, is attached on one side by its entire length to a twig, tree trunk, or other support.

Cynthia Moth
Other Common Names — Ailanthus silk moth, Chinese silk moth
Scientific Name — *Philosamia cynthia*
Family — Saturniidae (silkworm moths)
Order — Lepidoptera
Size — Length, 1 inch; wingspread 5¼ inches
Range — Introduced from China about 1861; well-established in eastern United States

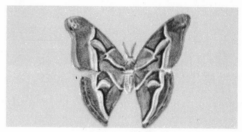

Cynthia moth

Cynthia moths are olive-green with a pinkish band and a whitish crescent on each wing. The pale green caterpillars are covered with a whitish powder and have blue and black tubercles. Their favorite food is ailanthus. The cocoons are similar to those of promethea but are larger, grayish rather than brownish, and less securely fastened. (*See Ailanthus*).

Io Moth
Other Common Names — None
Scientific Name — *Automeris io*
Family — Saturniidae (silkworm moths)
Order — Lepidoptera
Size — Length, 1 inch; wingspread, 2¾ inches
Range — Eastern United States north to

Io moth, male (above); female (below)

southeastern Manitoba, southern Ontario, Quebec, New Brunswick, and Nova Scotia

The hind wings of both sexes are bright yellow, each with a large eyespot. The front wings of the male are also yellow, but those of the female are reddish. The caterpillar is green with a reddish and a white line along each side. It is covered with spines that, when touched, produce a skin irritation. The thin cocoon is spun in leaves on the ground.

Luna Moth
Other Common Names—None
Scientific Name—*Actias luna*
Family—Saturniidae (silkworm moths)
Order—Lepidoptera
Size—Length, ¾ of an inch; wingspread, 4¼ inches
Range—Eastern United States except southern tip of Florida. North to southeastern Manitoba, southern Ontario, Quebec, New Brunswick, and Nova Scotia

Luna moth

The luna is considered the most beautiful of the silkworm moths. Each pale

green wing has a transparent spot; the fore wings are lined along the upper edge with purple; the hind wings end in long slender tails. The green larva is distinguished by a yellow line along each side and the small red tubercles are not silvered as in polyphemus. The cocoon is usually made between leaves on the ground.

Polyphemus Moth
Other Common Names—None
Scientific Name—*Telea polyphemus*
Family—Saturniidae (silkworm moths)
Order—Lepidoptera
Size—Length, 1¼ inches; wingspread, 5¼ inches
Range—Mexico north throughout the United States to the Canadian border and southern New Brunswick, and Nova Scotia

Polyphemus moth

This is a beautiful and exceedingly variable species, but the wings are usually some shade of buff. Each wing has a transparent spot near its middle, the one on the hind wing forming part of a large peacock eyespot. The bright green caterpillars are provided with small red tubercles that are silvered on their sides. The cocoon is commonly enclosed in a leaf, is usually not secured to the twig, and as a rule falls to the ground in the autumn.

Promethea Moth
Other Common Names—Spicebush silk moth
Scientific Name—*Callosamia promethea*
Family—Saturniidae (silkworm moths)

Promethea moth, male (above); female (below)

Order—Lepidoptera
Size—Length, 1 inch; wingspread 3½ inches
Range—Eastern United States except southern tip of Florida. North to central Manitoba, Ontario, Quebec, New Brunswick, and Nova Scotia

The most abundant of the silkworm moths, promethea is interesting because the sexes are colored so differently that they have been mistaken for different species. The wings of the male are blackish with a pale grayish border. Those of the female vary from reddish through brown to buff, and each wing has an irregular white line across the middle. The greenish caterpillar is about two inches long with small red, yellow, and minute black tubercles. The long, narrow cocoon is enclosed in a leaf, folded lengthwise. Before spinning the cocoon the larva binds the stem of the leaf to the twig with silk.

Recommended Reading

Field Book of Insects—Frank E. Lutz. G.P. Putnam's Sons, New York.
Insect Guide—Ralph B. Swain. Doubleday & Company, New York.

MOTHER CAREY'S CHICKEN (*See under Petrel*)

MOUNT MCKINLEY NATIONAL PARK
Location—Central Alaska
Size—3,030 square miles
Mammals—Moose, caribou, Dall sheep, grizzly bears, wolves, foxes, lynxes, martens, otters, minks, beavers, marmots, squirrels, porcupines, snowshoe rabbits, pikas
Birdlife—Golden eagles, bald eagles, geese, ducks, loons, swans, jaegers, shorebirds, songbirds, ptarmigans
Plants—Black spruces, tamaracks, birches, willows, Labrador tea, many wildflowers

Most of Mount McKinley National Park is above the timberline. The peaks of the highest mountain in North America tower 20,300 feet above sea level, dwarfing the nearly 300 other peaks of the Alaska Range which also lie within the park.

Bare rocks, snow fields, and glaciers give way to tundra, rolling expanses of arctic grass and moss. The wildlife, both on tundra and in woodlands, is extremely varied; 30 mammals and over 100 species of birds have been recorded there.
Accommodations—Mount McKinley Park Hotel and Camp Eielson (tenting); open June 10 to September 15
Headquarters—Within the Park; McKinley Park, Alaska

MOUNT RAINIER NATIONAL PARK
Location—West-central Washington
Size—377 square miles
Mammals—Elk, mountain goats, blacktail deer, black bears, coyotes, foxes, racoons, martens, beavers, marmots, snowshoe rabbits, pikas, mountain beavers
Birdlife—Golden eagles, bald eagles, saw-whet and pygmy owls, ptarmigans, grouse, band-tailed pigeons, three-toed and Lewis' woodpeckers, many songbirds
Plants—Firs, hemlocks, cedars, yews, spruces, many wildflowers

A volcanic cone that still emits threads of steam after about 400 years of inactivity, Mount Rainier, at 14,408 feet above sea level, is visible for nearly a hundred miles in all directions. Its higher elevations are never free of ice and snow, and it has more than twenty-five glaciers. The lower slopes are carpeted with huge

Most of the rugged peaks in Mount McKinley National Park rise above timberline

Mount Rainier, once an active volcano, rises above forests of hemlocks, spruces, and firs

trees, while the alpine valleys are a blaze of blossoms in spring and summer.

Roads and trails extend throughout the park, which is open in the winter for skiing and other sports.

Accommodations—At Longmire, Ohanapecosh, and Paradise Valley; numerous campgrounds

Headquarters—At Longmire, Washington

MOUNTAIN BEAVER

Other Common Names—Aplodontia, sewellel, boomer
Scientific Name—*Aplodontia rufa*
Family—Aplodontidae (mountain beaver)
Order—Rodentia
Size—Body length, 13 to 18 inches; tail, 1 inch; height at shoulder, 5 inches; weight, 2 to 3 pounds
Range—Coastal Pacific Northwest from southern British Columbia through Washington, and Oregon, to northern California. From sea level to over 9,000 feet

Never much valued, except by Indians who ate its flesh and made fur robes of its hide, the mountain beaver is a biological curiosity. Known to the loggers

as *boomer,* this little mammal of the Pacific Coast rain forests is a lone survivor of another age, a primitive type of animal whose range, more than a million years ago, extended over most of the western half of the United States. Today, this gopherlike creature is restricted to only about 60,000 square miles of Pacific slope country in California, Washington, Oregon, and southwestern British Columbia. Located structurally somewhere between the porcupines and the marmots, the mountain beaver is classified in a family all its own (Aplodontiidae).

Zoologists have been known to get highly excited at the sight of a mountain beaver, for anyone living outside the Northwest has small chance of seeing a live one. In 1945 the Portland, Oregon, Zoo claimed to be the only one in the world able to keep a mountain beaver alive for more than two years.

The stockily built mountain beaver looks and acts like a pocket gopher. Are they pugnacious? To find out one should try to take a live mountain beaver

The stockily built mountain beaver resembles an oversized pocket gopher both in its appearance and its habits

from a trap sometime. The male and female look alike, their fur a chestnut to reddish-brown, with a sprinkling of black hairs, especially along the middle of the back.

A gardener near the Pacific Coast forest edges may glimpse a mountain beaver cutting a choice currant stem or cabbage plant, for the animal will occasionally come out of its burrow to feed during a dull, heavily overcast day, but this broad-headed, thick-necked animal is essentially nocturnal, feeling its way around in the night more with the aid of its long, sensitive whiskers than with its poor eyesight.

Its abode in the wooded Pacific Coast mountains, foothills, and lower canyons is easy to find. Often it will be in the rich soil of an alder and vine-maple flat close to a bubbling spring. More likely, because of the importance of drainage in this wet climate, its extensive burrowings will be found upon a hillside above a flat or a stream, but seldom very far from water.

To find one, one looks for clumps of sword ferns from which the choicest fronds have been severed. At first glance this appears to be the work of commercial fern pickers, but there are no human footprints in the animal trail beneath the plants. A look around will disclose the fern tips stacked neatly in the entrance of a mountain beaver burrow.

Before other entry ways one may find a variety of vegetation—the tips of blackberry canes, salal, grasses, mahonia leaves. Perhaps a whole Oregon grape bush will be pulled into a tunnel opening, plugging the hole like a cork, or one will see chips from a rotted log dropped by the mountain beaver along its runways.

Local folks say ot the neatly stacked herbage that the mountain beaver is curing its hay for the winter food. Others claim it will use it for bedding. If one digs into its tunnel, he will find it lined with dried plants.

Mountain beavers are able to climb trees but seldom do so

Upon the hillsides, under the cool damp forest, mountain beavers' tunnel entrances dot the slope. One might think, if one does not know the little animal, that he has found a large colony of them, but usually no more than a male and female and perhaps their young ones live there, for mountain beavers are only slightly more sociable with those of their own kind than the solitary pocket gophers.

The main tunnels, averaging 6 to 10 inches in diameter, are 8 to 12 inches below ground, and may be as much as 200 to 300 feet long. The tubes are connected by short passages and with the surface by numerous openings through which the mountain beaver pushes its excavated dirt.

Perhaps it is sleeping in one of its grass-lined bedrooms, or a burst of energy may be driving it to build another tunnel. The mountain beaver builds extravagantly, but follows the line of least resistance; in one place branching out for a succulent morsel, in another following the underside of a convenient log, where it need build only half a tunnel, or perhaps crossing a short space above ground.

A mountain beaver has two projections upon the heel of each forefoot, which help it to handle its food. It sits up, squirrel-like, and pushes its food back between its rapidly crunching molars. Its long, sharp teeth are able to sever a ¾-inch stem with one slash. It will climb trees up to 15 feet in height, sometimes cutting off the branches as it climbs; it can girdle a tree a foot in diameter. Toss a mountain beaver into the water and it will readily swim ashore. Cage one with one of its fellows, and instantly there is a fierce battle for supremacy.

Admirably equipped for digging, its legs are short and powerful, the claws on the front feet are long and strong. Using its chest, shoulders, and broad, blunt head and propelling itself with its hind feet, the mountain beaver pushes masses of soft dirt ahead of it. Excavating a nest chamber about the size of a three-gallon bucket, it lines it with dried grasses, twigs, and leaves. This chamber is usually at the end of a blind tunnel, or, occasionally, in an enlarged portion of a main passageway. There, in March or April, after a gestation period of one month, the female mountain beaver gives birth to the litter of two to five pale brown, big-headed young. They are born blind and at two to three months of age, they leave their mother. Maturing slowly, they weigh only three-quarters as much as their parents at the end of their first winter. They do not attain sexual maturity until their second year.

What does the mountain beaver do when the heavy winter rains flood its tunnels? It has apparently lived on the coast long enough to get used to the heavy rainfall. During the rainy season, when prolonged downpours send water rushing down its tunnels, the mountain beaver goes about its business as usual, splashing up and down the passageways. If the tunnels fill completely, it swims out and finds a drier spot. If snow falls, it builds its tunnels through the snow.

In the virgin wilderness the mountain beaver has plenty to eat—the bark and foliage of willow, alder, hazel, dogwood, maple, elderberry, currant, gooseberry, ferns—and it is kept within a normal population by its natural enemies, the cougar, wildcat, skunk, owl, coyote, and most dangerous of all, the mink and weasel, which pursue it below ground in its burrows. In the burned-over and cut-over land, a jungle of shrubs, herbs, vines, and the tangled masses of logs give it protective cover from predators, but it is there also that the forests of the future are being planted by commercial foresters.

These tree farms furnish a plentiful food supply for the mountain beaver. On a winter's night it will follow up a row of tiny, hand-planted trees and strip the bark from each to get at the succulent fiber on the inside. Even a Douglas-fir, six inches in diameter, is not safe, for the mountain beaver will uncover the roots and strip them, thus killing the tree.

Foresters say that the mountain beaver's phenomenal increase is the direct result of predator control in which the cougar, wildcat, coyote, and other natural enemies of the mountain beaver have been destroyed. In the absence of predators, in order to control the mountain beaver, foresters must rely upon vigorous trapping campaigns (*see under Predation*).

In addition to foresters, other people protest against the mountain beaver. A housewife writes an indignant letter to a Pacific Coast newspaper, claiming that mountain beavers have eaten all her marigolds, bleeding hearts, and nasturtiums. Raspberry growers add their voices to the protests. Mountain beavers like raspberry canes, often cutting and

Willow growths at the edge of coniferous forests are a favorite habitat of the mountain beaver

carrying away nearly the entire hedge. Vegetable and fruit growers discover mountain beaver damage to their farm crops—onions, clover, carrots, and young fruit trees.

The Pacific Coast Indians no longer depend upon mountain beavers, but in the past these animals were an important source of food and clothing to them. The men and many of the women wore a single robe, which covered about half of the body from neck to knee. A few of their finer robes were made of the true beaver (*see Beaver*) and the priceless sea otter, but generally, it was the mountain beaver's skin that furnished the Indian's covering.

It was one of these robes that originated the white man's confusion as to the proper Indian name for the little animal. The Indians brought to the American explorers, Lewis and Clark, robes made from mountain beaver skins, saying in Chinook, "She-wallal." They were referring to the robe, but the explorers thought they meant the animal that furnished the skins. Lewis and Clark classified the animal as a squirrel, because of its flat, gnawing teeth, and called it sewellel, a name still applied to it frequently among naturalists.

To the Yakima Indians the mountain beaver was squallal; to the Nisquallys it was showt'l. Sh'auch is another Indian name for this creature. To many a pioneer the mountain beaver was just a big ground squirrel, to others it was a marmot. Many present-day citizens of the Pacific Northwest do not know of its existence. —E.H.

MOUNTAIN LION(*See under Cougar*)

The white-footed mouse lives in forests as well as in prairies and deserts. It is a nocturnal mammal and lives on a diet of seeds, insects, and, in fall, acorns

MOUSE

The word *mouse* is a general term used to refer to a large group of small rodents that have several common characteristics. These small animals have compressed lower incisors, no premolar teeth, and tails that are usually naked or scaly. The rats are members of the same group of families but are generally larger.

New World mice are assigned to three families—Cricetidae (mice, rats, voles, and lemmings); Heteromyidae (pocket mice, spiny pocket mice, kangaroo mice, and kangaroo rats); and Zapodidae (jumping mice). Actually the difference between mice and pocket mice, spiny pocket mice, voles, and lemmings is slight, the distinction being made on the basis of biological characters that are often not readily apparent to the untrained eye; therefore, most of these small rodents are called "mice."

In addition to these native species the Old World mice are represented in the New World by the house mouse, *Mus musculus*. This species is classified in the family Muridae and has reached the New World from Europe and Asia on ships. It has successfully established itself nearly everywhere where man lives (*See also Lemming, Kangaroo Rat, Muskrat, Rat, Rodent, and Vole*).

As a group, mice (and rats) are, in sheer numbers, probably the most abundant of all four-footed creatures. It is estimated that in North America alone they supply one-fourth of the total mammal population. The New World mice inhabit every type of habitat—woodlands, prairies, and arid deserts. The house mouse of the Old World has adjusted its habits to take advantage of the food and shelter available wherever man has built homes, warehouses, markets, barns, or other structures.

The Sanskrit word *musha*, from which the English word *mouse* is derived, means thief and is a fitting description of the house mouse that long ago took up its one-sided partnership with man in Europe, Africa, and Asia. Most North American mice, however, have little to do with man and spend their lives in fields and forests spending their nights ferreting out insect larvae, nibbling on shoots and roots, dealing with problems of territorial rights, or trying to evade a host of enemies—owls, foxes, shrews, and even other mice (*See under Mammal: Mammal Study*).

Even though a few species have on occasion caused severe damage to crops during population "explosions," or have caused heavy losses of trees in orchards by girdling their trunks, and a few carry diseases that they transmit to swine and man, most of these little creatures are harmless. In fact it has been demonstrated that the sheep forage in a California field was increased five times by the soil stirring activities of kangaroo rats (*See Kangaroo Rat*).

As a source of food for carnivores, mice, because of their fecundity, are highly important in the food web relationships of most wildlife communities (*See Buteo*). Many species of mice produce three, four, or five litters a year. The white-footed, or deer, mouse (*Peromyscus*), under ideal conditions in a cage, has produced up to 15 litters in a year. The young mature rapidly and soon begin to breed and produce a ready source of energy for many kinds of snakes, birds, and mammals

The pocket mice (*Perognathus*) are a group of 18 to 20 species that inhabit arid and semiarid regions. There is some evidence that they do not hibernate, nor do they often drink water. This moisture is supplied from their chief food—seeds—in metabolic processes. These mice are solitary except during breeding periods and probably do not live more than about two months, primarily because of predation upon them by hawks, foxes, and other carnivores. The spiny pocket mouse, *P. spinatus*, is an abundant

species in arid southern California and Baja California.

Five of the fifteen species of harvest mice (*Reithrodontomys*) inhabit North America north of Mexico. Harvest mice molt twice before they mature and probably shed their coats annually thereafter. These small mammals are at home in humid coastal regions, grasslands, or tropical forests. They prefer a habitat where grasses are available in sparse growth, and they build small, globular nests above the ground in clumps of this vegetation.

The North American species of harvest mice include the Plains harvest mouse, *Reithrodontomys montanus;* the Sonoran harvest mouse, *R. burti;* the western harvest mouse, *R. megalotis;* the saltmarsh harvest mouse, *R. raviventris;* and the fulvous harvest mouse, *R. fulvescens.*

The three North American species of red-backed mice are short-tailed little rodents that inhabit the northern coniferous forests and extend southward in the mountain ranges of the United States. They are somewhat diurnal and are most active during the hours just before night and after daybreak. They have become scarce in several areas because of extensive cutting of coniferous trees.

The northern red-backed mouse, *Clethrionomys rutilus*, inhabits Keewatin, Mackenzie, and Yukon territories in Canada, and most of Alaska. Gapper's red-backed mouse, *C. gapperi*, dwells in the northern coniferous forest belt from Newfoundland to British Columbia and in the mountain ranges of the eastern and western United States; while the western red-backed mouse, *C. occidentalis*, is limited to the coastal forests of western North America from British Columbia to northern California.

The distribution of the four species of tree mice (*Phenacomys*) coincides with the occurrence of certain coniferous trees. These rodents are never very abundant and have localized enclaves within their ranges. The dusky tree mouse, *Phena-comys silvicola*, is restricted to Tillamook and Benton counties on the coast of Oregon. The northern tree mouse, or heather vole, *P. intermedius*, ranges from Newfoundland to British Columbia and northward in the Rocky Mountains and Sierra Nevada. The coast tree mouse, or white-footed vole, *P. albipes*, lives in the forests of coastal Oregon and northern California, while the red tree mouse, *P. longicaudus*, ranges along the coast from northern California to central British Columbia.

The red tree mouse is the best known of these species and inhabits humid spruce-fir forests. Male red tree mice live in underground burrows or in litter on the forest floor, but climb up into the trees and build small nests there during breeding periods. The females are wholly arboreal and build larger nests of twigs and needles in the lower branches usually away from the trunk. Sometimes they will occupy the abandoned nest of a squirrel.

At birth the red tree mouse weighs one-ninth of an ounce and is naked. In 19 days it is fully furred and its eyes are open. The young mouse becomes fully independent in about one month.

The food of red tree mice consists of the tender middle sections of fir needles. The twigs are often cut and stored.

Although the distribution of tree mice coincides with that of spruce, not all of the species live in trees. The northern tree mouse dwells in grassy forest meadows or at the edges of tree growth. It also inhabits areas where heather or sagebrush grow.

In Cochise County, Arizona, the southeastern corner of that state, lives the northern pygmy mouse, *Baiomys taylori*. This little creature is active at night and eats seeds and various parts of green plants. Unlike most rodents, male pygmy mice help the females care for the young, and will carry them back to the nest if they become detached from the mother outside.   —G.A.B.

Grasshopper Mouse
Other Common Names — None
Scientific Name — *Onychomys torridus*
Family — Cricetidae (mice, rats, voles, and lemmings)
Order — Rodentia
Size — Body length, 4¾ to 6½ inches; tail, 1½ to 2½ inches; weight, up to 2 ounces
Range — Northern Mexico and Baja California, north in arid regions of western Texas, New Mexico, Arizona, southern Nevada, and south and central California

Grasshopper mice have long ears, white bellies, and relatively thick, tapering, short tails. They are somewhat of a paradox, because, though rodents, they are largely meat-eaters. In captivity specimens get along nicely on a diet of mealworms, with some seeds for variety. Under natural conditions they live largely on insects and other small, invertebrate animals. Years ago, Vernon Bailey, an American naturalist of the United States Biological Survey, now called the United States Fish and Wildlife Service, made exhaustive laboratory studies on these interesting little rodents. One of his mice was allowed to make nightly visits to the kitchen where it soon ate all the cockroaches that came out at night.

"At first the roaches were numerous and large, but after a few weeks they became scarce, and only the very small or young individuals were occasionally seen," wrote Bailey. He found that if the cage of his captive mice was placed in a closed room at night, with the cage door open, that the animals would return to their nest box after their nocturnal forays.

Among the rodents, the grasshopper mouse is something of a miniature "hound dog." According to scientists, it puts its nose to the ground and efficiently "smells out" its prey. Its other senses appear equally acute. Bailey wrote that these rodents could hear insects walking when they could not see them. In addition to invertebrates the little rodents kill and eat larger mice. When they are hot on the trail of their prey they become very excited and shake their short tails vigorously.

Grasshopper mice make their nests in burrows dug by other animals. There three to six naked young are born with their eyes and ears tightly closed. Three weeks later when the eyes and ears are open the young are clothed with soft fur. According to one authority, if the nest is disturbed, the young hold tight to their mother's teats while she drags them to safety.

Somewhat larger and darker colored than the southern grasshopper mouse is the northern grasshopper mouse, *Onychomys leucogaster*. It has a less limited range and dwells throughout much of the western United States.   —E.I.

Jumping Mouse
Woodland Jumping Mouse
Other Common Names — Kangaroo mouse
Scientific Name — *Napaeozapus insignis*
Family — Zapodidae (jumping mice)

Order — Rodentia
Size — Body length, 7½ to 10¼ inches; tail, 4¾ to 6½ inches; weight, ½ to 1 ounce
Range — Southern Newfoundland, Quebec, Ontario, and southeastern Manitoba. Also, northeastern United States from northern Minnesota, Wisconsin, northern and eastern Michigan and northeastern Ohio, east to Atlantic Coast. South to Pennsylvania and in limited distribution to northern Alabama and Georgia

Modified for specialized bipedalism the woodland jumping mouse has greatly enlarged hind limbs and tiny forefeet. Its exceptionally long, finely tapered tail serves to balance and steer its body in its flying leaps. This mouse has a yellow coat, darkened on the back in a broad band, and snow-white feet and underparts. In North America the woodland jumping mouse is the only species that truly hibernates during the cold winter months.

The grasshopper mouse has a short, thick tail that looks as though it were cut off at the middle

When startled, the woodland jumping mouse makes a prodigious leap of several feet and then hops away on an erratic course

This harmless little nymph of the meadows and woodlands cannot be charged with one bad trait. It is primarily a seed-eater but loves to climb the brambles for berries in season and often its dainty white hands and chubby face are stained with fruit juices. There are two distinct species of jumping mice in America: One favors the meadows and marshes (the meadow jumping mouse) while the other (the woodland jumping mouse) haunts the woodlands and mountain streams and has an even longer tail with a white tip. The woodland jumping mouse can cover 10 or 12 feet in one leap and is credited with exercising a curious eccentric dance during the breeding season—it bounces up and down like a ball on an elastic string, seemingly without any apparent motive.

In addition to the woodland jumping mouse, three species are classified in the genus *Zapus*. The meadow jumping mouse, *Zapus hudsonicus*, inhabits most of the eastern United States (except the extreme South) west to Colorado and Montana, and in Canadian forests it is found from Newfoundland to British Columbia into southern Alaska. The western jumping mouse, *Z. princips*, is primarily a species of the northwestern states south to mountainous New Mex-

ico and north into western Canada. The Pacific jumping mouse, *Z. trinotatus*, is limited to the coastal regions of northern California, Oregon, and Washington, and inland to southern British Columbia.

—G.G.G.

Pale Kangaroo Mouse
Other Common Names—Pygmy kangaroo rat
Scientific Name—*Microdipodops pallidus*
Family—Heteromyidae (pocket mice, kangaroo rats, and allies)
Order—Rodentia
Size—Body length, 5¼ to 7¼ inches; tail, 2¼ to 3¼ inches; weight, ½ to ¾ ounce
Range—Central Nevada extending into eastern California

Habits of the Pale Kangaroo Mouse

It is a banner day for the student of small mammals in California when he livetraps a pale kangaroo mouse, *Microdipodops pallidus*. This mouse is relatively rare in California although it may be quite common in its favored habitat. If prefers to live in the sandy sagebrush areas that are found in the extreme eastern strip of California close to Nevada. For a long time pale kangaroo mice were thought to be extremely rare in the sagebrush and drifting sand of Nevada as well. Raymond Hall, an American mammalogist, attributes this apparent rarity to the collecting methods of mammalogists of the early 1900's. He says that in the 10 years before and after the turn of the century, field naturalists traveled by horseback or with horse-drawn vehicles; therefore it was necessary for them to make overnight trapping stops close to water and green forage. Since the kangaroo mice prefer a dry, arid habitat, the early-day Nevada collectors took few specimens. Later when automobiles were used by collectors it was possible to make dry camps in the arid sagebrush areas and the catch of kangaroo mice greatly increased.

Very few people ever see kangaroo mice. They are strictly nocturnal and, unlike their relatives, the kangaroo rats and pocket mice, they are seldom tempted by the baits ordinarily used to livetrap small rodents. Collectors report that even when they are enticed into traps they are so nimble that they are often able to take the bait without springing the trap.

In common with the kangaroo rats, pocket mice, and pocket gophers, kangaroo mice have external fur-lined cheek pockets in which they probably transport seeds to their nests.

Kangaroo mice resemble kangaroo rats in having strong hind legs, weak, poorly developed front legs, and densely furred soles on their feet. However, they are much smaller in size and the tail lacks the dark ventral stripe, white lateral stripes, and tuft of longer hairs on the tip that characterize most kangaroo rats.

The scant vegetation of the arid sandy area in which it lives plays an important part in the life of the kangaroo mouse. Beneath the sage and rabbitbrush it builds its burrow. From the seeds of the blazing star, wild buckwheat, lupines, and desert plantain it garners its food. To the kangaroo mouse, as to the grasshopper mouse, drinking water is relatively unimportant. Neither needs to drink. Both obtain necessary water for body processes from the metabolic water that results from the digestion of dry seeds. The sagebrush and rabbitbrush likewise provide a haven where it can hide from owls, coyotes, and bobcats.

Like many other animals that live in this dry, arid habitat, kangaroo mice leave their burrows only at night when the relative humidity close to the ground is highest. After a night of foraging, the animals return to their burrows. Whether the drifting sands cover the entrance to the hole or whether the rodent actually pushes a plug of sand into the entrance is not known. However, soon after dawn the burrows are closed, evaporation from the nest is retarded, and the little creature settles down to rest.

The tracks of kangaroo mice, although smaller, are very similar to those of kangaroo rats. They leap rapidly over the sand, using the strong hind legs to push while the tail serves as a balance. The stiff hairs on the soles of the feet probably keep the animal from sinking into the soft sand. That they are great jumpers is evidenced by the observation of Hall who reports that a captive mouse jumped out of a container 17 inches high and 10 inches in diameter without touching the sides.

There is very little known about the life history of the kangaroo mouse. At present two species of *Microdipodops* are recognized—the dark kangaroo mouse, *M. megacephalus*, and the pale kangaroo mouse, *M. pallidus*. Whether or not a distinction between these two species will remain valid after detailed distributional studies remains to be seen.

—E.I.

White-footed Mouse
Other Common Names—Deer mouse
Scientific Name—*Peromyscus leucopus*
Family—Cricetidae (mice, rats, voles, and lemmings)
Order—Rodentia
Size—Body length, 6 to 8¼ inches; tail, 2½ to 4 inches
Range—Most of the United States, north to southern Maine, southern Michigan,

The agile white-footed mouse often prowls in trees for seeds and buds

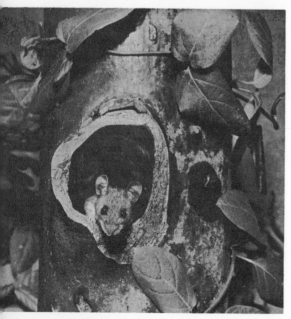

A white-footed mouse peers out from its house in a tree hollow

and North Dakota, extending into the southern prairie provinces of Canada; west to Alberta, northeastern Wyoming, central and southern Kansas, extreme southern Colorado and eastern Arizona; south to North Carolina, northern Georgia, and southeastern Louisiana; extending into Mexico to Yucatan

Deer mouse is another name for this small rodent, an animal much more appealing in appearance than its city relative, the house mouse. A brown and white coat, large ears, and big eyes give it this name. Although this species is found only in wooded and brushy areas, other types of white-footed mice inhabit all of North America including the deserts and prairies. These mice are prolific little creatures, raising several litters of three to seven young each summer. Their nests are usually in hollow trees or stumps, but sometimes they may appear in such surprising places as a camper's rucksack or mattress.

A variety of tiny items make up their diet, including nutlets, raspberry seeds, clover seeds, fruits, and insects. Active throughout the year, white-footed mice seldom are seen because of their nocturnal habits. They are continually hunted by owls, weasels, bobcats, and foxes against which their only defense is constant alertness. White-footed mice are an important part of the diet of many valuable furbearers. Although they occasionally become a nuisance to some campers and around cabins where they seek bits of food, these little creatures are an economic asset in their destruction of forest insects that are often harmful to forest trees (*See Food Chain; and Biological Control*). More than a dozen species of white-footed mice inhabit North America.

The deer mouse, *Peromyscus maniculatus,* lives almost everywhere in North America south of the arctic tundra except the extreme southeastern and southwestern United States.

MOUSE (*See Vole for Meadow Mouse*)

The white-footed mouse has large ears and eyes. Its short-haired tail is often as long as its head and body

MUDFISH

Other Common Names — Bowfin, dogfish, grindle, spottail
Scientific Name — *Amia calva*
Family — Amiidae (bowfins)
Order — Amiiformes
Size — Length, up to 2½ feet
Range — Very common in Mississippi River and its tributaries. Range throughout the area bounded by Great Lakes drainage, Vermont, Florida, and Texas.

The mudfish's body is stout and lizardlike. Its mouth is large and is armed with sharp, strong teeth. The dorsal fin is long and has 45 to 51 rays. The anal fin is much shorter and has 9 or 10 rays.

The fish's back is dark olive-green or yellowish-green. The sides are lighter, and the belly is a creamy green. A prominent dark spot is present at the upper base of the tail fin of adult males.

The mudfish eats live things of all kinds. It is particularly destructive of other fishes and for this reason should not be artificially introduced into new waters as some people do by using young mudfishes as bait. Mudfishes are not sought after as game fishes but are often unintentionally hooked. They are not particularly good table fish, although they are sometimes eaten.   — M.R.

MUFFLEJAWS (*See under Fish: Common Freshwater Fishes of North America*)

MULBERRY

The mulberries belong to a family of plants (Moraceae) that includes also Osage orange and hemp. Mulberry trees are planted both for ornament and for their fruits, which are highly attractive to birds. Two species of mulberries are native to the United States — the widely distributed red mulberry, *Morus rubra*, and the Texas mulberry, *Morus microphylla*, which grows as a small tree or shrub in the arid Southwest. The white mulberry, *Morus alba*, introduced from Asia, is a hardy species; the introduced

The leaves of red and white mulberries often vary in form

black mulberry, *Morus nigra*, grows in the South. About 59 kinds of North American birds eat mulberries.

The leaves of the plants in the family Moraceae are somewhat lobed and broad. The flowers are in different catkins for each sex. The fruit is an aggregate, a cluster of seeds each surrounded by an edible pulp.

The osage orange, a small to medium tree, native to Texas and Oklahoma, was spread throughout the prairie states as a living fence. The fruit is inedible.

— G.B.S.

MULBERRY
Red Mulberry

Other Common Names — Mulberry
Scientific Name — *Morus rubra*
Family — Moraceae (mulberry family)
Range — Florida to Texas north to Vermont, New York State, southern Ontario west to Minnesota and South Dakota
Habitat — Rich woods
Leaves — Of several shapes, margins with rounded, lobelike teeth
Bark — Light yellowish-brown, with narrow grooving
Flowers — Inconspicuous little tassels up to one inch long, appearing with the new leaves

Fruit—1 to 2¼ inches long blackberry-like, dark purplish—black or red when ripe

MURRE
Common Murre
Other Common Names—Foolish guillemot, tinker, scout
Scientific Name—*Uria aalge*
Family—Alcidae (auks, murres, and puffins)
Order—Charadriiformes
Size—Length, 17 inches
Range—Coastal, Arctic south to Nova Scotia, and North Pacific south to central California

Northern seabirds in the Alcidae, or auk family, murres are colonial nesters on sea cliffs overlooking cold waters. The eggs taper to a blunt point, a factor that may keep them from rolling off the rock ledges where they are laid. Two weeks after hatching, the young birds tumble down the cliffs and into the sea, where the parents attend them until they can fly.

The common murre has a long, slender bill, which is the chief point of differentiation between it and Brunnich's, or thick-billed murre.   —G.B.S.

MURRELET
The four murrelets (ancient, marbled, Kittlitz's, and Xantus') are members of the auk family, the Alcidae. Others in the group are the puffins, murres, guillemots, and auklets. Birds of the cold northern Pacific, they feed on small fishes and crustaceans.

Murrelets are small, none of them more than 10½ inches in length. They nest on rocky islands off the coast, or on coastal mountains above the timberline. During the summer months they occur singly or in pairs, but in winter they often gather on the Pacific Ocean in small flocks.   —G.B.S.

Mystery of the Marbled Murrelet
Out of the misty night from the darkening surge of the Pacific, small, fast-flying bodies hurtle over the headlands and disappear into the hinterlands of western North America. Their destination still may be one of the last mysteries of the bird world, for up to the late 1950's, no man had ever traced the route from sea to nesting grounds of the marbled murrelet. Nor had anyone studied its nesting habits, or seen its newly-hatched young.

The common murre nests in closely packed colonies

Authorities in ornithology of the Pacific Northwest had little to contribute apart from theories. Allan Brooks, J.A. Munro, I. McTaggart Cowan, Harry S. Swarth, Kenneth Racey, S.G. Jewett, H.M. Laing, R.M. Stewart—all keen, determined workers and wise in the ways of birds—in all their studies had not unraveled the mystery of this common little alcid. Much is still to be learned about *Brachyramphys marmoratus,* as it is known to science, the dipchick as it is commonly called, or the marbled murrelet as it is known to birdwatchers.

The first egg of the marbled murrelet known to science was taken from the oviduct of a bird shot by G.G. Cantwell on the Prince of Wales Archipelago on May 23, 1897; subsequently others were gotten in the same manner. There are also two records of eggs said to have been taken *in situ,* that is, where laid. Unfortunately, these two records are contradictory and are not accepted by ornithologists.

The first report was of an egg found on rocky land above the Tien River about 70 miles north of Nome, Alaska. A.H. Durham, the collector, is said to have taken this egg and the two parent birds on June 10, 1904. Later, in 1931, S.J. Darcus published the discovery of several nests situated in burrows in the ground on the Queen Charlotte Islands. Unfortunately, no birds were collected with these eggs and some ornithologists claim the eggs collected by Darcus are those of the ancient murrelet, a common and well-known nester in the area. No one questions the integrity of these workers, but since neither has followed up and proved his finds, science could not but regard the nesting habits of these birds as still a mystery.

Fishermen, natives, settlers, and loggers of coastal British Columbia, and amateur ornithologists have added bits of information. Many of these have offered leads—many were contradictory. The following is an account of what was known about the marbled murrelet up to the late 1950's.

It is a small seabird approximately 10 inches long and weighs about half a pound. It lives more on the inner coastal waters than do most other members of the family Alcidae to which it belongs. It eats small crustacea such as euphausid shrimps, and fishes such as the sand launce, which it catches by diving after them. Its numbers upon the coast are legion; during the summer it is in all the offshore waters from the Aleutian Islands of Alaska south to Washington, and in the winter it moves as far south as California.

In summer the marbled murrelet is a dark mottled brown; in winter it appears dark on the back, with white underparts. The molts take place in spring, in late February, and March; in the fall, in September and through October. During the molts, it has a peculiar mottled appearance, intermediate between the summer and winter plumages. The name dipchick stems from the diving habit of these birds. Generally riding low on the water, its tailparts up, it dives with a sudden flip, momentarily exposing a white rear as it disappears below the surface.

Marbled murrelets move about at night, to and from their terrestrial nesting grounds, and their daylight hours are spent on the sea. During the breeding season they become agitated as daylight fails, anxious, it seems, to be off to the nesting area in order to relieve the incubating mate, or to feed the young one, as the case may be. It seems that they may have only one young, as adults collected have but a single brood patch. In addition, when the young appear on the sea, only one is usually seen accompanied by the two parent birds.

The young appear to be raised in the nest until capable of flight. At that time they are in a plumage resembling that of the winter adult and are, consequently, easily distinguished from their brown-colored parents. They often retain vestiges of a grayish natal down adhering to the ends of feathers about the head and back; the egg tooth may still be prominent on the upper mandible. In studies of the breeding colonies of seabirds, a characteristic pungent odor has been noted on those that occupy burrows, an odor often persisting for days after scientific specimens of the birds have been skinned and preserved. This odor is not present on the marbled murrelet young when they first arrive upon the sea, which might suggest that this species does not nest underground.

Many theories have evolved as to the nesting place of the marbled murrelet. First, and quite naturally, it is thought that it may use a burrow; many birds of this family do excavate burrows in the ground and raise the young therein. A great deal of study has been done on the known breeding colonies of seabirds in British Columbia. Rev. J.H. Keene, W.H. Osgood, W.A. Newcomb, Brooks, Swarth, Stewart, Walter Maguire, and C.J. Guiguet have all thoroughly worked Cox and Langara Islands in the Queen Charlotte group. In addition Frederick, Hippa, and many of the smaller islets along the west coast of the Charlottes have been covered but to date (apart

Langara Island (left) and Graham Island (right), of the Queen Charlotte group, are possible nesting sites of the marbled murrelet

from the questionable Darcus record) no one has ever found a marbled murrelet in an underground burrow.

On the Queen Charlottes the Haida Indians take many birds and their eggs from the breeding colonies for food. These natives have been questioned, shown specimens of the marbled murrelet, and asked, "Where does she lay her egg?" Invariably there has been the same reaction—the slow captivating native grin, or a chuckle, accompanied by a shake of the head and a "nobody knows." These natives know their birds. They excavate far more burrows than do any museum collectors. They do it year after year. If there were any marbled murrelets nesting in burrows close to the coast these people would have uncovered them long ago.

The tree theory—that they nest in hollow trees, or high in the branches or under the roots of trees well inland—sounds logical enough when one has spent a few evenings near the ancient murrelet colonies and seen these web-footed seabirds perched on the limbs of Sitka spruce. However, the great stretches of logged-over land, thousands of square miles from sea coast to mountain top, in many sections of the breeding range, should have produced records of the marbled murrelet when the operators were denuding the slopes. Each species known to nest in the coniferous forests has been reported many times— why not the marbled murrelet? It seems unlikely that this species nests in the coastal forest.

Some ornithologists—Laing of Comox, for example—believe that the murrelet is a cliff nester, breeding on the face of inaccessible mountain chasms, much like the black swift. The black swift is a common bird, and yet the total number of nests found can be counted on one's fingers. There are many cliff faces in the coastal range that could conceivably offer suitable niches for nesting murrelets. Many of these close to the sea have been examined with no success. The moun-

taineers of British Columbia are an active lot, and many of them are bird lovers as well. People like the late Don Munday and his family, who have climbed such coastal mountains as Saugstad and Waddington, have nothing to report. Moreover, most ornithologists agree that structurally the murrelet is not adapted for clinging to cliff faces. For these reasons and the fact that most cliffs near the sea have been examined by various ornithologists interested in falcons and other cliff dwellers, with no marbled murrelets reported, it would seem that the marbled murrelet does not nest there.

Ronald Stewart, a topnotch field man and resident ornithologist on the Queen Charlottes, once put forth the theory that the answer might be found about large freshwater lakes in the interior of Graham Island. It was reported to him by a native friend that marbled murrelets had been seen taking off at dawn from Eden Lake, near the head of Naden Harbor. These birds, the Indian said, circled to great heights and then headed for the sea. To strengthen his theory, Ronald Stewart recounted a record of an egg taken from the oviduct of a bird shot at Harrison Lake on the lower mainland of the Province many years ago. This record has never appeared in the literature, but Stewart actually saw the specimen. Freshwater lakes are numerous in the coastal area, and they abound with trout. Consequently, fishermen prowl many of these lakes, yet have never reported seeing marbled murrelets there. Also, if the birds nested in burrows leading from the water, muskrat trappers should have taken marbled murrelets long ago. If they nest on the ground, in the marshes, or on the banks, such men as J.A. Munro of the Dominion Wildlife Service, would surely have discovered them in the course of their waterfowl investigations. While it is possible that lakes may play some part in the life history of these birds, it seems unlikely that they nest in close proximity to such bodies of water.

The mountain-top theory, put forth on the strength of the nesting habits of the Kittlitz murrelet, a very closely related form, seems logical, and biologically the idea is sound. The story of the Kittlitz murrelet is an interesting one. For many years the breeding habits of this alcid were unknown, too. In 1913 F. E. Kleinschmidt, who was collecting specimens of birds at Pavloff Bay, Alaska, asked his guide if he knew where the bird nested. The Aleut guide pointed to the towering skylines and said "way far, on top of mountains, in the snow."

Kleinschmidt must have taken this information with a large grain of the proverbial salt, although a local trapper corroborated the guide's statement. Later, he chanced to be up on the skylines hunting brown bears for the Carnegie Museum. In order to approach one, he took a circuitous route up through some snowfields. As he stalked carefully towards the bear, a bird flushed from a small patch of gravel that the receding snows had left. There, at his feet, was the first egg of the Kittlitz murrelet ever found in the nest.

It may be that the mystery of the marbled murrelet will be solved in a like manner. Certainly the birds are often at great heights on their way to and from the sea—but here again there is contradictory evidence. Marbled murrelets have been seen flying in low over the timber, and occasionally directly into the timber. At Masset, where Stewart, Maguire, and Guiguet have watched them returning northward to the sea at dawn, the country to the south is flat, and on the ground in those flat woods Stewart once found a fully feathered young one. Stanley Jewett, in Oregon, also found a young marbled murrelet; this was also in a timbered area. McTaggart Cowan at the University of British Columbia picked up a young one on the campus in front of the library.

All of these birds may or may not have been many miles from the nest in which they were hatched. All of them were in full juvenal plumage and were theoretically capable of flying. Whether they had been injured in flight, and had dropped from exhaustion, or were near the nest site prior to take-off, is unknown. Had these three birds been on the sea, no questions would have arisen, but their presence on the land, apparently uninjured, raises another problem, a point to be considered, weighed, and evaluated in the piecing together of evidence that will ultimately lead to the discovery of the marbled murrelet's nest. Jewett and others record the interesting find of E.J. Booth, who discovered a partially incubated marbled murrelet egg on the south fork of the Nooksack River in the State of Washington. There was no evidence of a nest of any kind, but the fact that the egg was about two-thirds incubated eliminated the possibility of it having been accidentally dropped where it was found. Here was evidence that ties in nicely with the theory that the immature birds found by Stewart, Jewett, and Cowan may have been near the place of hatching. It suggests also that these alcids may, perhaps, nest in a variety of habitats.

In July 1946, Ronald Stewart told of a great concentration of marbled murrelets in Masset Inlet on the Queen Charlotte Islands. These birds, some 200, were watched for a day. All were in breeding plumage and all were feeding on sand launces, a small silver fish shaped like a lead pencil, and about the same size. As dusk approached the murrelets began to rise off the water and fly, circling to heights of perhaps 500 feet. Still circling they would drop back into the water, the whole flock giving their weird little calls.

When darkness had almost descended some rose to great heights and disappeared inland to the west, others took off low over the water, gradually rising until they were lost in the gloom to the south. All of them were "packing feed" in their bills, and the silver sand launce showed up in the darkness seconds after the birds themselves were lost to sight. Subsequently such concentrations have been seen on three occasions, at Cumshewa Inlet on Moresby Island, at Frederick Island, and near the mainland on the Bardswell Islands. In each case the first concentrations of young birds were seen on the sea the following morning. A very exciting possibility existed in this behavior, for in a breeding concentration of adults feeding young, might lie the key with which to unravel the mystery.

The latest evidence up to the late 1950's received at the British Columbia Provincial Museum was of great interest. A stunned marbled murrelet was taken from the debris of a large hemlock felled on the Queen Charlotte Islands in 1953. The logger, Walter Feyer of Masset, a reliable amateur birdwatcher, examined the murrelet and found it had a brood patch. Further search in the debris uncovered the fragments of a marbled murrelet's egg, but no evidence of a nest of any kind was found. That no nest was found was not important, for many birds do not gather material and build nests. However, there *was* a bird and a broken egg in the debris of that tree. Whether the tree had fallen upon a nesting site, or whether the egg and the bird were in the tree before it was felled is not known. But there seems little doubt that Walter Feyer was very close to a nesting marbled murrelet that day. Unfortunately, he was unable to uncover further evidence.

Thus, as far as was known, the nesting behavior and nesting habitat of the marbled murreled remained unsolved, and presented an intriguing problem to ornithologists.   —C.J.G.

MUSHROOM (See under Fungus)

MUSKEG

The Muskeg Farthest South

Bird students enrich their experiences by making long journeys to new places and climes; they may do as well by making shorter journeys to new habitats. By no means the least interesting of these is a muskeg, with its sea of mosses, its trembling aspens, and its rich association of northern wildflowers. The one large area of true muskeg in northern United States is the great wilderness just north of the Red Lakes of Minnesota, the place where woodland caribou are making their last stand within the boundaries of the United States. Fortunately, however, there are small detached portions of muskeg country nearer and more accessible to most people, for example, the Cranberry Glades of Pocahontas County, West Virginia (*See also under Bog*).

If one goes there as a long June day draws to its close, the twilight is brought to throbbing life by a chorus of thrushes—hermits, Swainson's, and veeries (*see under Thrush*).

If one works down the slope toward the glade level, mourning warblers sing from every tangle where, a little time before, had stood a virgin forest of red spruce. In the scattered groves of young spruce, winter wrens bubble out their melodies, and golden-crowned kinglets and brown creepers call softly. From the ultimate twig of a fire-scarred tree an olive-sided flycatcher gives its strongly accented, three-note whistle, while nearby a flock of purple finches chatter melodiously.

Down along a trout brook where hemlock, spruce, alder, birch, and aspen are entangled the warblers abound—northern waterthrushes, Canada warblers, magnolias, and others. Red-breasted nuthatches call, and juncos flit about, the white feathers in their tails opening and closing like animated pairs of scissors. And high overhead a raven calls hoarsely.

Break through the last fringe of aspen and alder, and one steps out onto the glades, the muskeg itself. Stretching ahead is the treeless area, a springy mat of sphagnum and reindeer moss covering the ground, the moss itself overgrown with cranberry and creeping

Lady's slipper abounds in muskeg habitats

dewberry. Here and there are low shrub patches, mostly bog rosemary, and the herbaceous species include occasional orchids—grass pinks, snake's mouth pogonias, and twayblades—buckbean, goldthread, and sundews.

The Cranberry Glades of West Virginia, are in a latitude farther south than Washington, D.C. This is the muskeg farthest south.

The Cranberry Glades, about six hundred acres in extent, occupy a mountain valley between two folds in the higher Allegheny Plateau. At the valley level the elevation is about 3,400 feet, and the surrounding mountains rise to 4,600 feet. Local belief—entirely without geological support—is that the Glades represent a late plant succession stage in a filled up lake. The Cranberry River and its tributaries ramify widely throughout the region, the drainage being through a narrow gap. Formerly the forest was practically pure red spruce, but all mature timber was removed during the early years of the present century, and the new forest growth is mixed, with pure spruce stands only on the higher mountain ridges. Yellow birch, hemlock, red maple, quaking aspen, mountain ash, and beech are common trees in the rather scrubby existing forest.

On the mountain slopes near the Glades is the Appalachian Forest, that wonderfully rich mixture of tree species which partakes of both North and South. Hemlock, spruce, and yellow birch meet and mingle with Fraser's magnolia, tulip poplar, hickories of several species, oaks, and black walnut. Basswood, beech, maples of four species, and black cherry are all present. On the forest floor is an herbaceous flora that is likewise of mixed affiliations. The animal life tells the same story—here is a true expression of the Transition Life Zone in the best sense of that term.

The northern birds include saw-whet owl, northern pileated woodpecker, yellow-bellied sapsucker, alder, least, and olive-sided flycatchers, northern raven, brown creeper, winter wren, red-breasted nuthatch, hermit and Swainson's thrushes, veery, golden-crowned kinglet, golden-winged, Nashville, parula, magnolia, Cairns's, black-throated green, Blackburnian, chestnut-sided, mourning, and Canada warblers, northern waterthrush, rose-breasted grosbeak, purple finch, pine siskin, savannah and swamp sparrows, and the Appalachian forms of the blue-headed vireo, slate-colored junco, and black-capped chickadee.

This would be a very respectable list for many a point in southern Canada. When one turns to the southern forms of birdlife in the Cranberry Glades, there are such species as red-bellied woodpecker, Acadian flycatcher, Carolina chickadee, tufted titmouse, Bewick's wren, Carolina wren, blue-gray gnatcatcher, white-eyed vireo, worm-eating, Kentucky, hooded, and, possibly, prothonotary warblers, Louisiana waterthrush, and yellow-breasted chat. No northern locality is likely to match this combination.

Birds at the extremities of their range are always interesting, and it is worth noting that such species as saw-whet owl, hermit and Swainson's thrushes, Nashville and mourning warblers, northern waterthrush, and purple finch are here at their southernmost known breeding station in eastern United States. The common, or Wilson's snipe may breed locally and this would add another species.

Scientists have not been neglectful of the Cranberry Glades. The region has been the subject of biological studies of various kinds and degrees of thoroughness for about 80 years.

The summer biological expeditions of West Virginia University spent a week in the area each summer for many years. Alexander Wetmore and the Smithsonian investigators worked there in making their West Virginia collections. Wetmore made the Glades the type locality for the Mississippi song sparrow, *Melospiza melodia euphonia*, and Remington

Kellogg did likewise for the West Virginia flying squirrel, *Glaucomys sabrinus fuscus.*

Besides the squirrel, other mammals of special interest that are more or less common in the territory include starnosed mole, *Condylura cristata;* cinereous shrew, *Sorex cinereus cinereus;* smoky shrew, *Sorex fumeus fumeus;* water shrew, *Sorex palustris;* mountain mink, *Mustela vison vison;* cloudland red squirrel, *Tamiasciurus hudsonicus abieticola;* cloudland white-footed mouse, *Peromyscus maniculatus nubiterrae;* Allegheny wood rat, *Neotoma magister;* Stone mouse lemming, *Synaptomys cooperi stonei;* Carolina red-backed mouse, *Clethrionomys carolinensis;* Smoky Mountain rock vole, *Microtus chrotorrhinus carolinensis;* Roan Mountain woodland jumping mouse; *Napaeozapus insignis roanensis;* Virginia varying hare, *Lepus americanus virginianus;* and New England cottontail, *Sylvilagus transitionalis.*

Five major open areas (the Cranberry Glades proper) occur in the 600-acre vale, each with its own character. Every opening is surrounded by dense fringes of alder, and through these fringes run meandering streams, the muddy banks and stream beds making crossings rather difficult. The stranger to the area (and even the initiated) will do well to orient himself by sun or compass before he attempts to thread one of these fringes from one glade to another. He will not be able to see landmarks, cannot follow streams successfully, and, although he will not get lost, he may very well lose his destination as well as his point of departure.

Most visitors will reach the Glades region by means of a Forest Service truck trail (usually closed to vehicles). In this first glade border may be found some of the rarer or more interesting plants of the region, the tiny Small's twayblade orchid, attractive Van Brunt's polemonium, and the round-leaved sundew. There will certainly be a chorus of swamp sparrows, if time and season are right, since the sedges of this glade are favored nesting sites for these birds.

Beyond Flag Glade the visitor will be pretty much on his own. If he bears to the left, through a heavy alder fringe and over a slightly drier ridge covered with quaking aspen, he will find Round Glade; if he continues straight ahead through another heavy alder thicket he will come upon Big Glade; if he inclines sharply to the right he may find Little Glade, the smallest of the five.

Round Glade, about twenty acres in extent, is famed for its moss hummocks. Here the mosses (*Polytrichum* and *Sphagnum*) have convoluted until one has the impression of a green sea whose low waves were suddenly frozen. Some waves are three feet or more from trough to crest. Two species of cranberries cover the moss, and near the woodland borders creeping snowberry *Chiogenes* and dwarf cornel *Cornus canadensis*, are to be found. These forest fringes are also favorite places for olive-sided flycatchers and many species of warblers.

Bit Glade has an open surface of over fifty acres, and is about a mile in extent. It epitomizes the whole area at its best; here are the finest sphagnum beds, the most extensive incrustations of reindeer moss, *Cladonia*, the showiest orchid displays, and birding as good as can be found in the region. At the far end of the opening is a wonderful bed of buckbean, *Menyanthes*, most attractive, of course, during its season of flower. In the low shrubs which invade the glade, marsh hawks nest. Savannah sparrows build in grassy tufts out on the open area.

The most difficult of the glades to reach is Long, a comparatively narrow opening which lies to the northeast of Big Glade, on the left as one reaches the far end of that opening. Long Glade is protected by the widest, densest, and wettest alder borders, is least visited and most likely to yield botanical surprises.

Casual visitors who work their way from one glade to another, and who wish to return on approximately the same course will do well to tie a handkerchief or some other conspicuous object to the alders at the point where they break into each new glade. This makes for easy return. It is well to bear in mind that all parts of this alder fringe look alike when one is inside of a round or oval opening.

As may possibly have been gathered from this account, West Virginians are inordinately proud of the Glades, and they have been known to stray somewhat beyond the bounds of strict accuracy in reporting certain conditions and happenings purported to obtain locally. One may as well admit it—misinformation concerning the area has burgeoned to the point where a story about the Glades needs only to be fantastic to be believed.

The orchids of the Glades region have been much talked about. An enthusiastic local newspaper article gave publicity to the orchid display some years ago, and it was amazing to watch the story grow. The first story, if somewhat overdrawn, was within the bare neighborhood of truth, but presently it was picked up by a state daily, in whose columns the orchids grew in number to "over a hundred species" (about three times as many as are to be found in the entire state). This wasn't the end by any means. A Pittsburgh paper, casting about for a Sunday feature to vary its usual line of exposes of the more or less private lives of more or less notorious people, hit upon the orchid story. In these metropolitan columns there proceeded to unfold a flower paradise where "over *two thousand* kinds of orchids are to be found!" Why should the botanical explorer go to Java or the upper Amazon?

The truth is this: During late June and early July there is a very nice display of snake's mouth and grass pink orchids, *Pogonia* and *Calopogon,* about some of the glade fringes. In early August there are some spectacular clumps of yellow-

A naturalist examines the nests of the blue-gray gnatcatcher

fringed orchids, *Habenaria ciliaris.*
Throughout the summer are to be found
a half-dozen smaller and less conspicuous
species. There are good colonies of pink
and yellow lady's slippers in some of the
woodlands around the Glades. Yet so per-
vasive is this orchid fame that during
a world's fair about two thousand of the
blossoms, mostly grass pinks, were collected and distributed on "West Virginia
Day." This act of patriotic publicity
pretty well wiped out the colonies in
more accessible places—any good Michigan bog could have furnished the same
number of blooms without serious loss.

The winter is severe at this elevation,
sometimes with four feet of snow. Spring
comes slowly, the early shoots of the
skunk cabbage furnishing a feast for the
bears which abound. The openings a
little later blaze with marsh marigold,
and the thrushes return to take up their
singing. Summer comes abruptly and
pours out its riches of plant and animal
exuberance. In the autumn the sphagnum beds turn red, brown, yellow, or
purple, contrasting with the somber gray
of the reindeer moss. At this season the
local people come in to harvest cranberries, some of them also harvesting the
piece de resistance for a woodland ban-
quet in the form of a wild turkey.

And what of the future of the Glades?
The area is within the Monongahela National Forest; furthermore, it has been
given a high priority recreation rating.
This means that the truck trail will

*A flying squirrel at Cranberry Glades
pauses before soaring to another tree in
search of food*

*A pair of Acadian flycatchers tend their
nest in Cranberry Glades*

probably remain closed to the public;
the access roads will pass through forests unadorned by the Orchid Gardens
Beer Spot or Ye Olde Cranberry Glades
Hotdog Stande.

These scattered islands of quasi-Ca-
nadian forest and bog life in the southern Appalachians are doubly precious
in that they are so unexpected. The town
dweller with an urge to go to the North
makes a vertical rather than a horizon-
tal journey to the Canadian woods. At
the Cranberry Glades the hermit and
Swainson's thrushes will sing just as
sweetly as along the Restigouche or
the Miramichi, and, although the fish
that he catches will be smaller, he
may go through a long June day without ever seeing a mosquito or a black
fly.

This comparative freedom from summer insect pests is the crowning glory
of the lakeless southern Appalachian
region. One actually goes camping in
June without mosquito net or fly dope.
There are some deer flies and occasionally the black flies are troublesome.
"No-see-ums" are a nuisance on calm
and humid evenings, but the mosquitoes
are, generally speaking, nonexistent. A
June day there (or for that matter one
in July or August as well) can be that
rare thing of which the poet sings,
simply because the flies may be rarer
than the day.   —M.B.

MUSKELLUNGE (*See under Pike*)

MUSK-OX
Other Common Names — None
Scientific Name — *Ovibos moschatus*
Family — Bovidae (cattle, sheep, and goats)
Order — Artiodactyla
Size — Male: body length, 5 to 6 feet; height at shoulder, 4 to 5½ feet; weight, 500 to 700 pounds. Females somewhat smaller
Range — Coastal, eastern, and northern Greenland, Queen Elizabeth Islands, Franklin, northern Mackenzie and Keewatin, Northwest Territories, Canada

The musk-ox, one of those species which had dwindled in numbers so as to be in danger of extinction, at present lives in the wild only on the northeast coast of Greenland and in arctic barrens directly north and northwest of Hudson Bay as far as about latitude 83° north, or within 400 or 500 miles of the North Pole. Even within this range musk-oxen live only in certain areas, there being large expanses where none occurs. Although today there are no native wild musk-oxen west of the Mackenzie River, there is sufficient evidence from parts of skeletons that have been found, and from stories of the Eskimos, that a few of the animals inhabited Alaska as late as about 1850. At that time the species undoubtedly lived over most of arctic North America and northeastern Greenland. Whereas in those days the number of musk-oxen in existence probably numbered in the hundreds of thousands, now a high estimate would be 20,000 individuals, most of which live on the arctic islands.

Physical Appearance
The musk-ox is an odd-looking hoofed mammal that resembles a small, shaggy-haired miniature buffalo. It combines certain features of cattle with those of the sheep, but is in no sense a connecting link between them. Stocky in build and short-legged, a large male measures about 7 feet long, stands a little over 4 feet high at the shoulders, and weighs about 550 pounds. The female is smaller. A hump on the shoulders of the animal reminds one of the bison. Its tail is only three or four inches long, its ears are small, and its eyes rather prominent. Its head is broad and heavy; its face wide and short. The male carries thick down-curved horns, the broad flat bases of which nearly meet over the forehead to form a frontal shield. The horns of the female are smaller.

How It Got Its Name
Although it is not a true ox, the peculiar buffalo-like appearance of musk-ox prompted the name ox, and the prefix musk had its origin in the characteristic musky odor of the animal. The Eskimos call it the *oo-ming-mack;* the Chipewyan Indians, *et-jer-ray*. Most species of mammals are known by various names, but *musk-ox* is its universal name known to white men, though in olden times it was sometimes called the musk bison or musk buffalo. Even in other languages than our own the term musk-ox can be literally translated. For example, in French, the name is *le boeuf musque*.

One might well surmise that any animal adapted to such uninhabited regions as the arctic barrens would be safe from human molestation. To enter the domain of the musk-ox, one must take a journey by plane, or by ship amidst arctic ice fields, or else travel by canoe and foot through many miles of Canadian wilderness. Parching winds, cold, and possibly hunger may greet the hunter. Often, miles of search are necessary to locate a herd of musk-oxen, for even in an area known to be inhabited by them they live in small scattered groups that shift their range in following the changing food supply. This gregarious habit, this tendency to gather in herds, is a marked instinct in the musk-ox, though the groups are usually small ones of from 10 to 30 or 40 individuals,

Musk-oxen live in small herds on the northeastern coast of Greenland and in the arctic barrens

quite in contrast to the huge herds of bison that formerly contained thousands in a gathering. Search for food may induce musk-oxen to wander many miles, but there is no regular seasonal movement of migration, such as is likely to occur in a species that congregates in immense herds or flocks.

Food Habits

Grass is the principal food of the musk-ox, though it frequently eats willow browse, small flowering plants, and particularly, in summer, the tender shoots of the dwarfed shrubs of its homeland. It is supposed not to like lichens or mosses, but a Mr. Hoare in an old report for the Canadian Government, says: "The plain on which these musk-oxen had been feeding was windswept and only about two inches of snow lay on it so the top of the vegetation was plainly visible. It was evident that the musk-oxen had been feeding on several varieties of moss and lichens which the

barren land caribou commonly use as winter food . . . . On one side of the moss-covered plain was a gentle slope on which bunch grass could be seen sticking up through the snow. Up this slope the musk-oxen had evidently passed, without cropping any of the grass, to the mossy ground above. There was also a thick growth of coarse hay a short distance away on the opposite bank of the river. Grass, willow tips, and flowering plants were quite accessible in the district had the musk-oxen preferred these sorts of fodder."

In the winter, herbs and all vegetation of the Barren Grounds are often covered with snow. It is then that the powerful hooves of the musk-ox come into play. as it paws away the snow to obtain its food. At this season it quenches its thirst by eating snow, since all fresh water is frozen over.

Aggressiveness of Bulls in Summer

The bulls become rather pugnacious

during the summer, and frequent battles ensue between them. Hoare describes a combat that he watched: "About nine o'clock on the night of June 26 I was resting my pack on a big rock about three miles up Hanbury River when I saw three large musk-oxen feeding in a hay meadow across the river from where I was. They had not seen me so I quickly got behind the rock and went into camp by getting into my sleeping sack. From there I could watch them comfortably without being seen. After some little time two of the three animals stopped feeding, walked out of the wet meadow to some higher dry ground and began circling one another with lowered heads, as if for battle. Each then placed its heavy, horn-protected head against that of its opponent and tried to force it back by main strength. After a short while of this, with little success to either side, each animal backed away a few paces and ran with lowered head at the other. They came together with considerable shock. Three times they met, with little advantage to either. Then each backed away until they were about 25 paces apart. In their new positions they stood glaring at each other for a few moments, then, as if at a given signal, each bounded at the other on the same instant, gathering speed as they went, and met with such impact that both were knocked back some distance, one on his haunches. The victor stood in fighting attitude for a short while, then, receiving no further opposition from the vanquished, went and lay down. The other soon followed suit. The third musk-ox which seemed to be larger than either of the other two, seemed to pay not the slightest attention to the battle but went on feeding in the meadow."

During the breeding season in August the males are particularly combative, and fight each other for control of the females. They do not breed until four years old. As with some of the other herding mammals, polygamy is the rule, and each successful bull has a harem of about 10 cows. Sometimes 2 or 3 bulls with their harems gather together into one herd of 30 animals.

Birth and Growth of Young

The baby musk-ox is born in May or early in June and lies for a while hidden in moss or snow. One calf to a mother every other year seems to be the rule. Blackish-brown except for a white patch on its forehead and white feet, it is a curious little fellow covered with fuzzy hair or wool. At birth it weighs only about 16 pounds, but at that it is well developed and within a few hours follows its mother.

When a calf is six months old, little knobs that form on the forehead indicate the beginning of the horns. By the time a male is 15 months old these knobs have grown into straight horns about six inches long that protrude parallel with the ground. As the horns continue to grow they broaden at the base and bend down and forward in a graceful curve, the ivorylike tips pointing upwards.

Defense Against Wolves and Man

Excepting man, and occasionally a bear, the wolf is the only real threat to the musk-ox. The herding instinct, however, is a great protection to the musk-ox, and even the wolf is not often successful in its attack on a group. Several wolves in a pack may at times best a single animal that wanders from the gang. An attack on a herd is a different matter, for the musk-ox has a method of defense that defies its enemy. At the least suspicion of approaching danger the bulls surround the calves and cows, and, with heads out and lowered, face the wolves in regular battle array. The cows later may join the battle front, and what a front it is! Each head has a heavy bony shield flanked by two sharp horns that with a single upward thrust might disembowel an unwary wolf and leave it prostrate. No wise wolf would approach such a fortress.

The sharp, downcurved horns that flank a bony shield across the heads of male musk-oxen are used to defend the herd against its natural enemy, the wolf

Thus, the musk-ox is well adapted to fight its natural enemies of the Barren Grounds. From outside, however, came white men, entirely foreign to the musk-ox and its country. Armed with rifles, they had no need to fear that threatening battle formation of horns and shields, for they could kill from a safe distance. Herds of musk-oxen were slaughtered without mercy. Now that the species is almost gone, laws and regulations have been passed and reservations set aside for its protection. Conservationists hope that it is not too late.

Although robust and clumsy in appearance, the musk-ox is not slow on foot, and it can run swiftly. It is able to run up steep hills with surprising ease and speed, and could well escape many of the attacks of man if it chose to run away rather than to stand its ground. Eskimos have long hunted musk-oxen for food and clothing, but until the use of the rifle against musk-oxen, the killing among the herds had never endangered the existence of the species.

First Captive Musk-oxen

The meat of the musk-ox is nourishing and tastes like tough beef, but some white men who have eaten it say that it has a peculiar musky taste that they do not relish. The pelt of the musk-ox is of very little value to civilized man, because it is too coarse in hide and hair for him to wear. Eskimos find it valuable for clothing because of its great warmth.

In all the attempts to domesticate the musk-ox no reference is made to studies on the subject by others; no apparent effort is made to profit by the experience of others in attempting to raise the musk-ox, no measure is taken of all known factors, bad as well as good, in determining procedure. Musk-oxen may be seen in a few of the larger American zoological parks, where once they become acclimated they may thrive moderately well. The first captive musk-ox in America was exhibited in the New York Zoological Park, where it arrived from arctic America on March 12, 1902. In this same zoological garden the first baby musk-ox ever born in captivity arrived September 7, 1925. Others have been kept captive in northern European countries, and the governments of Norway and Iceland have experimented in rearing them without success. The Dominion of Canada through protection of the musk-ox in its native environment has increased its population on the Thelon Game Sanctuary, northeast of Great Slave Lake, Northwest Territory, since the establishment of this range in 1927. The only comprehensive study on the musk-ox in captivity was that made by the Fish and Wildlife Service in Alaska.

In April 1927 the Legislature of the Territory of Alaska sent a memorial to the United States Senate and House of Representatives urging favorable action in appropriating funds to reestablish musk-oxen in the range formerly occupied by them in Alaska. During May 1930, under the active leadership of Senator Peter Norbeck of South Dakota and Representative C.C. Dickinson of Iowa, an appropriation of $40,000 was granted for the project. Administration of it was assigned to the Bureau of Biological Survey, United States Department of Agriculture, now the Fish and Wildlife Service, United States Department of the Interior. It was impossible at that time to obtain live specimens of any of the races of musk-oxen that lived in North America. It was necessary to buy stock of the Ward's musk-ox, which inhabits northeast Greenland. An order was placed with Johs. Lund, Aalesund, Norway, and late in August 1930 word was received that 34 animals, including 19 females and 15 males, had been captured. All were under two years of age and about half of them were calves of the year.

In a news release dated September 9, 1956, the United States Fish and Wildlife Service reported that the herd of wild musk-oxen on the Nunivak Island National Wildlife Refuge in Alaska had increased from 31 established there to 126 animals. Although the Fish and Wildlife Service had succeeded in reestablishing musk-oxen in their ancient habitat, it concluded, after years of study, that it is not practicable to raise them for wool production or other commercial uses.   —H.H.J.

MUSKRAT
Other Common Names — Musquash, Hudson seal
Scientific Name — *Ondatra zibethicus*
Family — Cricetidae (New World rats, mice, voles, and lemmings)
Order — Rodentia
Size — Body length, 10 to 14 inches; tail 8 to 11 inches; weight, 2 to 4 pounds
Range — Practically all of North America south of the limit of vegetation in the

The muskrat is at home along streams and in ponds and marshes in nearly all of North America

Arctic; absent from the southeastern United States, from southern North Carolina to western Florida; south-central Texas, southern Nevada, central Oregon, and California, except for the Colorado and Sacramento valleys and extreme northeastern counties

The muskrat is just what its name implies—a rat with a musky odor. The musk is supplied by two glands, located at the base of the tail. The musk is used by the muskrat as a means of communication. It is usually secreted at landing places along the shore, where it is believed to serve as a sort of scent station announcing to other muskrats that one of their kind has recently been there. Some feel that this musk plays an important part in attracting the sexes, but observations on this point are inconclusive.

Ponds, streams, and marshes, wherever they occur from Atlantic to Pacific, from the Gulf to the Arctic Ocean, are the natural homes of the muskrat. According to Ernest Thompson Seton, only the gray wolf and the red fox, among native North American mammals, have as great a range as the muskrat. An open, sunny or shallow, reed-choked end of a little pond is a favorite haunt. There, amid the cattail stalks—where redwings sing and long-toed mud hens scoot over the oozy swampland muck, where puddleducks (the mallards and blacks) tip up to feed, where the marsh hawk soars—this is muskrat territory.

From some vantage point beside the marsh, particularly at dusk, one may expect to see a brown-furred, ratlike creature scurrying through the tall reeds, or swimming along an open channel with only nose and back protruding above the water. When it crawls out on dry land it will look like an enormous meadow mouse, a mouse as big as a cottontail rabbit, with a long vertically flattened tail. It will probably be gnawing on something, perhaps a bit of cattail stalk or sweet flag root. The conspicuous four long front teeth (two above and two below) proclaim it as a member of the order Rodentia (animals that gnaw). These "chisels" are the muskrats prize possession. They procure its food, help build its house, landing platforms, eating huts, and serve as its principal weapons. The muskrat sharpens its teeth by using them. The more it gnaws, the keener the edge. This is because the inner side of the teeth is made of softer material than the outside, and so wears down faster (*See also under Beaver*). Since its teeth grow continuously, their length, in spite of use, is fairly constant.

The muskrat is an aquatic artist. An excellent swimmer and diver, it can travel on the surface, swim submerged, or crawl on the bottom in shallow water. It can remain underwater for a number of minutes without coming up to breathe, and is well built for life in wet places. The fur coat is warm and waterproof, and the big, partly webbed hind feet, with hair-fringed toes, make fine swimming paddles, and also good mud shoes. The long, flattened tail serves the muskrat as a rudder and as an oar for sculling. Its mouth can close behind its big front teeth, leaving them free for underwater work, such as getting out submerged roots, or gnawing a doorway beneath its haycock house. Some authorities believe that the muskrat's ears and nose constrict when it submerges, but observations on this point are lacking. These adaptations for getting along in water are very similar to those of the beaver. Ernest Thompson Seton calls the muskrat "little brother to the beaver." The activities of these two mammals are much the same except that the muskrat does not build a dam.

Muskrats are seldom seen in bright sunlight, excepting occasionally in winter. It is early in the morning before it is quite light, and again towards evening that they are most active. For this reason one usually first learns of their presence by evidence of muskrat activity —narrow channels through the marsh, burrows in low banks, small haycock-shaped mounds rising a few feet above water. These mounds are muskrat houses made of dead cattail stalks and mud. At first they are solid piles of cattail and mud, chiefly cattail, above water. Later a tunnel is dug beneath and a sleeping room is excavated several inches above water level. The doorway is a plunge hole into the tunnel below. However, when a bank is convenient, a burrow usually replaces the haycock house as sleeping quarters. Ponds and marshes usually lack banks for burrows, and many rivers have too swift a current for haycock houses. The muskrat's dwelling house must conform to its surroundings. The den, whether along the burrow or in the haycock, is furnished with a thick bed of dry leaves. This is the muskrat's winter quarters, and also the nursery where the young are reared.

Leading from the sleeping den and radiating through the swamp are muskrat channels. These are swimming lanes during spring high water, often dry runways in summer, and iced-over swimming tubes in cold weather. They are the streets of muskrat town and are the usual routes followed by muskrats in securing their food.

The muskrat "day" is largely taken up with the business of eating. It is, for the most part, herbivorous and finds much of the plant world around it good to eat—even parts of its own haycock house. Cattails, arrowhead roots or "duck potato", sweet flag, and wild iris, are among the staple items, but many other marsh plants, as well as plants growing on dryer land, including some cultivated forms, are also on the bill of fare. Even such surprising things as poison ivy bark and berries may be eaten by the muskrat, but it is not completely vegetarian. A muskrat may often have a meal of freshwater clams and leave small heaps of these shells, like miniature kitchen middens, scattered along the banks of streams. Remains of fish and

The muskrat has a scaly tail that is laterally flattened

amphibians have been found in its "kitchen garbage."

Since the den is a sleeping room and kept very clean, the muskrat does not eat at home. It has many dining rooms. These are usually under something; under an overhanging bank at the edge of the pond, in the doorway, or inside a winter eating hut. These last are "push-up" mounds of cattails, just big enough for one animal, and are scattered along the channels conveniently near the food supply. They serve the double purpose of affording shelter while feeding, and of maintaining openings through the ice in cold weather. Concealment is all important to the muskrat. Although ready to fight if cornered, its best defense against the mink, weasel, marsh hawk, and great horned owl is to keep out of sight. It is only when safely under a bank, or inside its "push-up" diner, that it can give full attention to its food. However, the animal may occasionally be seen eating in the open,

sitting on a log or small beach.

Since the days when America belonged to the Indians, the muskrat has been valuable to man. Its flesh is sweet and tender, its fur warm and durable. From the tail the Indian drew long fine sinews with which to sew porcupine quill trimmings on his moccasins and leather pouches. Today the muskrat is more valuable than ever. In many states it ranks first as a fur-bearer. Both from the standpoint of quality of fur and the quantity available, the muskrat rates as one of the most important fur mammals.

Since the word *muskrat* is such an unattractive, even repulsive name for a beautiful fur, most of these dyed pelts masquerade under the trade name of Hudson seal. The fur is usually prepared by plucking the long, outer hairs. The dense inner coat that remains is very thick and soft, like fur seal. As Hudson seal it is usually dyed black and makes a warm, handsome, fur coat. Similarly, muskrat is not a very pleasant name for a table dish. No one relishes the idea of eating "rat" meat, although the muskrat is no more closely related to the Old World rats we detest than dogs are to cats. "Marsh rabbit" or "Maryland terrapin" are much more delectable substitutes for muskrat steak and are the ones ordinarily used.

In addition to being of commercial value, the muskrat is important in its own right in relation to the other forms of life that comprise its habitat. Its flesh provides food for its enemies; its own feeding (plants and lesser animals) in turn, acts as a control on the numbers of these occurring in the area, but more particularly on the quantity of plants growing in the marsh. The muskrat eating huts and haycock houses offer readymade platforms for nesting ducks and other birds of the marsh.

An animal bearing such an important relation to other animals and to plants in its natural environment, and one so economically valuable to man, is deserving of a chance to live. That the muskrat survives today, in spite of extensive trapping, its natural enemies, and the draining of its swamp habitats, is due to its prolific nature. From four to nine young are the usual litter and, although information regarding the number of litters per year is inconclusive, it would appear that there are at least two, and frequently more, depending somewhat on the latitude. As many as five litters have been reported. Like other rats and mice, young muskrats are blind, naked, and helpless at birth, but grow and develop at an astounding rate. At six months the offspring are credited by some as old enough to have families of their own.

The demand for muskrat fur has been so great that man became impatient with the natural supply and attempted to operate muskrat farms as an industry. This is not as easy to do as it is with foxes and mink, which are more easily tamed and thrive well in the cages and runways. Nevertheless, muskrat

A muskrat haycock home

farming goes on, and there is now considerable literature on the subject.

Out in the marshes, streams, and ponds, where redwings nest, and other marshland habitants are busy with the important business of living, the muskrat builds channels, haycock homes, eating huts, rears its young, feeds, and is fed upon—a part of the natural balance of life in its watery realm.   —W.E.S.

Recommended Reading

American Mammals: Lives, Habits and Economies—William John Hamilton, Jr. McGraw-Hill Book Company, New York.
Field Book of North American Mammals—H.E. Anthony. Putnam's Sons, New York.
Lives of Game Animals—Ernest Thompson Seton. Doubleday, Doran, Garden City, New York.
Muskrats and Marsh Management—Paul L. Errington. Stackpole Company, Harrisburg, Pennsylvania.
The Mammal Guide—Ralph S. Palmer, Doubleday & Company, New York.
Muskrat Populations—Paul L. Errington. Iowa State University Press, Ames, Iowa.

MUSSEL(*See Bivalve*)

MUTATION (*See discussion of under Chestnut*)

N

NARWHAL
Other Common Names — Unicorn whale
Scientific Name — *Monodon monoceros*
Family — Monodontidae (white whale and narwhal)
Order — Cetacea
Size — Length, up to 16 feet
Range — Arctic seas

The long spirally twisted ivory tusk of the male narwhal is unique. The females are tuskless, and only one of the male's canine teeth, usually the left but rarely the right, grows into the functionless adornment.

In most respects the narwhal is like a small whale. Its young are easily confused with young white whales. It is predatory, living on small fishes, squids, and crustaceans and is hunted both for its ivory tusk and for the oil in its flesh.   — G.B.S.

NATIONAL AUDUBON SOCIETY
The history of the National Audubon Society is long and complex. The Audubon movement began in the 1880's as a protest against the slaughter of birds for their plumage and to stop the hunting of birds for sale in the public market, which had brought many species close to extinction. State Audubon Societies formed first, beginning with Massachusetts in 1896, but in 1905 these societies banded together to form the National Association of Audubon Societies, which became the National Audubon Society in 1934. Today the Society is concerned with the conservation of all natural resources.

As success was won in the field of legislation, attention was given by the society to a broader program of education. An elementary-grade education program known as the Junior Audubon Club, was begun in 1910 and made available to children throughout the country on a local school enrollment basis. Since 1918, when full records were first kept, more than 10 million children have been given field and classroom instruction in natural history with inexpensive National Audubon Society materials. This early exposure to a sympathetic attitude toward wild birds and other elements of our natural environment was an important foundation for the later development of a conservation conscience in many of these young people.

To help adults learn more about these same approaches, a number of summer camps were organized, beginning with the Audubon Camp of Maine in 1936 and now involving camps in Connecticut, Wisconsin, and Wyoming also, to provide basic, outdoors-oriented instruction in nature and conservation to many men and women who work as teachers or as leaders of youth group organizations.

As the years have demonstrated that

The use, if any, of the great tusk of the narwhal is unknown legal protection was not enough, a sanctuary system was established by the National Audubon Society for threatened bird and mammal species. Up to 1965, either through long term lease or ownership, the National Audubon Society maintained more than 30 sanctuaries that safeguarded many thousands of acres of strategic wildlife habitat. In the 1930's the Society undertook to study the basic needs of the more endangered species and it has since published important research reports on such birds as the flamingo, the roseate spoonbill, the whooping crane, the California condor, the golden eagle, and the ivory-billed woodpecker. These have been foundation stones in the effort to conserve America's threatened species.

In 1945 the Society initiated the branch Audubon Society plan so that interested citizens may form a local Audubon Society and be joint members of both the National and the local Audubon Society. There are now about a hundred such groups in the United States and, in addition, twice as many other state and local Audubon Societies affiliate themselves with the National Audubon Society and cooperate in advancing its broad objectives. In 1962, the National Audubon Society merged with Nature Centers for Young America, Inc. (*See Nature Centers*). Annual conventions are held around the country.

The National Audubon Society publishes *Audubon Magazine,* the successor to *Bird-Lore* that began publication in 1900; *Audubon Field Notes,* a journal of field ornithology to which amateur and professional birdwatchers contribute; and it also issues an important series of Audubon nature bulletins and nature charts for school and home use. The National Audubon Society has participated in the publication of *The Audubon Nature Encyclopedia* to bring to a new and larger group of the public basic information about natural history and the conservation of our natural resources.

The National Audubon Society is generally credited with having wielded a powerful influence for the conservative use of our treasured natural resources, especially in the wildlife field. It has been influential in fostering good conservation programs at the federal level; for example, in the setting aside of refuges important to such birds as the whooping crane and the California condor and in the creation of the Everglades National Park. Its programs have, directly or indirectly, molded much of that favorable conservation attitude which is part of the American climate of opinion today. In addition, the Society organized the International Committee for Bird Protection, and today participates in that Committee's program and in that of the International Union for the Conservation of Nature and Natural Resources.

The National Audubon Society operates on membership dues and generally uses only the income from modest investment funds to help balance annual operations. This is a challenging task, however, because the Society has assumed the obligation of being *the country's ecological conscience.*

Finally, though the National Audubon Society has a very real awareness of the tremendous obstacles that lie in the way of success in helping mold a public opinion that will include a high regard for the other forms of life that share the earth with us, it has faith that this can and will be done because it must be done.

Someone expressed this philosophy well when he said, in relation to the problem of preserving the rare California condor, "It is not so much that we *need* the condor, but that *we need to save it* because the attributes of wonder, humility, and selflessness that we must exercise in order to safeguard the existence of this and other rare species, are the very attributes we will need to exercise in working out our own survival as a civilization, even as a species."

The headquarters of the National Audubon Society is in New York City

Membership in the National Audubon Society is open to anyone interested in its work and ideals. Its headquarters are at 1130 Fifth Avenue, New York City 10028. (*See also under Sanctuary; Okeechobee; and Corkscrew Swamp*)

—R.C.C.

The Martyrdom of Audubon Wardens
Guy Bradley. On July 8, 1905, the first martyr to American bird conservation, Audubon warden Guy Bradley, was shot and killed on Florida Bay by two plume hunters he was attempting to arrest for shooting egrets in the sanctuary under his protection.

The chain of events leading to this tragedy was a long one, dating back to the commercialization of wild bird plumage. That this had become big business may be seen from the fact that in the egret nesting season of 1892 one among many feather merchants in Jacksonville, Florida, shipped 130,000 bird scalps (skins with the feathers on) to the New York market. Even though the hunters got only $1.25 per scalp for their work, if a thousand parent birds were shot at a heronry, the heartless effort seemed well repaid. That several thousand young

birds would starve to death in the nest because their parents were killed meant little to these men who killed with no thought of the future.

It was this disgraceful state of affairs that led conscientious citizens to organize Audubon Societies in a score of States, beginning with the formation of the Massachusetts Audubon Society in 1898. Later, a National Committee of Audubon Societies was formed (1905), and from this grew the National Association of Audubon Societies, and much later (1934), the National Audubon Society.

In May of 1901, William Dutcher, the first president of the National Committee went to Tallahassee, Florida, and successfully advocated the passage of a model, nongamebird protection law by the State Legislature.

To enforce the law, the governor of Florida appointed one game warden for each county. In areas like Monroe County, where vast stretches of mangrove and everglades wilderness were the home of countless herons and ibises, one warden could hardly be effective except locally. The Audubon Society therefore employed extra wardens at its own expense to help Florida protect these birds.

One of the first of these Audubon wardens was Guy M. Bradley.

Two plume hunters of Key West, accused of Bradley's murder, were brought before a grand jury, but released five months later because the prosecution failed to provide sufficient evidence.

In 1908 another Audubon warden, McLeod, was shot by plume hunters near Charleston, South Carolina. These deaths focused national attention on the bird protection effort, and in 1941, after a long struggle, the commercial use of all wild bird feathers was outlawed in New York State, the principal market for feathers, and it was soon afterward stopped everywhere.   —Ch.B.

NATIONAL FOREST (*See under United States National Forests*)

NATIONAL PARKS AND NATIONAL MONUMENTS

[The following article is reprinted from a booklet entitled *The National Park Wilderness* issued by the United States Department of the Interior, Fred A. Seaton, Secretary; National Park Service; Conrad L. Wirth, Director. —The Editor]

Wilderness is a physical condition, but it is also a state of mind. Both concepts are important—the former in matters of protection and management of wilderness areas, the latter in evaluating the benefits of wilderness. Both are important in planning for the intelligent and beneficial use of America's great cultural and recreational heritage.

The ideas we hold today about wilderness preservation in national parks are the result of many years of growth. The seed was planted long ago by those men who worked for the establishment of the first national parks. They saw a goal and pointed out a direction—but the entire concept did not emerge full grown at once.

Congress strengthened this movement and gave approval to it in the laws establishing national parks and the National Park Service. These laws, and accompanying tradition, form the firm base for the policies of today. However, the strength of the national park preservation movement derives less from them than from attitudes and beliefs that have evolved through the years among people concerned with national park matters. This includes a very substantial body of American citizens and their Congress, as well as the National Park Service itself.

The best safeguard of a principle is the peoples' understanding and appreciation of it, their conviction about it, and their dedication to it.

The Origin and Development of the National Park Idea

What is this modern preservation philosophy, and how has it developed? In 1864 Congress established a new pattern of public land use when it ceded Yosemite Valley and the Mariposa Big Tree Grove to the State of California, to be held inviolable for all time "for public use, resort, and recreation." But an event six years later marked the real beginning of the new pattern of thinking that set the destiny of the National Park System.

For six weeks, in 1870, a party of Montana citizens had been exploring with increasing awe, the remarkable country that today is known as Yellowstone National Park. At the end of the trail they sat around a campfire, talking of what should happen to this land in the future. And that group of practical-minded private citizens were so moved by the sight of strange natural wonders and the impact of primeval wilderness that they put aside all thought of personal gain. They then and there resolved that this wonderland should be forever preserved in public ownership, set apart as a national park for the use of all the people of America.

Three things in the establishment of Yellowstone are especially worth remembering. The first is that Yellowstone was envisioned as a *public* park, for public use and enjoyment. This was not a place to be locked up, isolated, and held from the people.

The second is this: The *public* park proposal came as a counterproposal *after* private ownership was considered and rejected. Preservation then meant primarily preservation against private control and commercial exploitation. The founders could hardly have foreseen that the natural wonders and the wilderness quality of this vast area could ever be endangered by the mere fact of public use; that preservation would come to mean preservation against overuse, inappropriate use, or overdevelopment; or that the park would need to be defended against competing kinds of public use. But, these are the major problems of the National Park Service today.

Erosion has sculptured bizarre formations at Bryce Canyon National Park, Utah

Third, Congress set aside the *whole* of Yellowstone, reserving not merely a geyser, a canyon, or a spectacular waterfall, but the total scene in all its vastness and variety. The men who defined the first national park were thinking in wilderness terms.

Other national parks followed, and again much of the moving force came from individuals who were inspired by their experiences in the wilderness they sought to preserve. One associates Colonel George Stewart and Gustavus Eisen with Sequoia and John Muir with Yosemite; William Gladstone Steele with Crater Lake; Enos Mills with Rocky Mountain; George B. Doerr with Acadia; Mark Squire and Dave Chapman with Great Smoky Mountains; and Ernest F. Coe with the Everglades National Park. Thus, to a very large degree, the motivation for the establishment of many national parks was a product of wilderness experience and wilderness appreciation.

Today, broad direction comes from a national office, but, for the development and protection of each individual national park or national monument, specific plans are made by the men who are closest to the natural scene—the superintendent of each park, his staff and professional aides. The inspiration of the wilderness continues to motivate the management of the national parks.

The Legal Basis for National Park Management

The laws which are, in effect, the Constitution of the National Parks, are:
The separate Acts of Congress establishing and pertaining to each of the National Parks.
The Antiquities Act of 1906 authorizing the establishment of National Monuments by Presidential proclamation.
The Act of 1916 that established the National Park Service.
While this Constitution may be subject to interpretation in the light of new knowledge and changing circumstances, its broad principles cannot be changed: That national parks are special areas—"dedicated and set apart . . . as public pleasuring grounds" to be retained in a "natural condition." Such words are found in the law establishing the first and all subsequent national parks.

The National Park Act of 1916 extends these same principles equally to the national monuments. There is no difference between a national park and a national monument in this regard—both are dedicated areas to be preserved for public enjoyment.

The National Parks Have a Single Purpose

Because the Act of 1916 is the basic authority and basic guide for the administration, protection, and use of all areas within the National Park System, it is worth our special attention. What does it really mean, and how does it apply to modern circumstances?

The key part of the act reads:
"The service thus established shall promote and regulate the use of the federal areas known as national parks, monuments, and reservations hereinafter specified by such means and measures as conform to the fundamental purpose of the said parks, monuments, and reservations, which purpose is to conserve the scenery and the natural and historic objects and the wildlife therein and to provide for the enjoyment of the same in such manner and by such means as will leave them unimpaired for the enjoyment of future generations."

The basic act uses the singular form of the word *purpose*—a single objective, not several. That single purpose inseparably combines *use* with *preservation*.
To isolate and emphasize either use or preservation to the exclusion of the other can seriously distort park planning, confuse park management and imperil the validity of the whole national park con-

cept. What, then, is the nature of this amalgam of use and preservation which we seek to define?

The National Park System is a national resource—a natural resource, a historical resource, a cultural resource. Like minerals, water, timber, and soil, it has value to man only when it is made useful to man.

Parks differ from other resources, chiefly in the nature of their products. Mines, timber, and cattle yield material products required by the nation. Parks yield the products of knowledge, refreshment, and esthetic enjoyment equally required by all people. The direct way, and essentially the only way, these products are obtained is through the intelligent and appropriate use of park resources by people.

Does this mean that the primary purpose of a National Park System is to provide pleasure, enjoyment, knowledge, and inspiration? Is this all?

Proper Use Depends upon an Unimpaired Natural Scene

How does preservation fit into this picture?

It fits in a most fundamental way, for the 1916 act is a clear recognition of a basic principle — the recreational, cultural, and inspirational products of parks are supplied by the natural scene, undamaged and unimpaired. To change the character of the park scene, or to modify or impair the natural environment, destroys a part of its capacity to yield those benefits to the human mind and spirit.

Preservation is not an end in itself, but a means to the kind and quality of enjoyment that the National Parks were established to provide.

The problem of today is not one of striking a balance between preservation on the one hand, and use, on the other. The basic problem concerns use itself. What *is* appropriate park use? The answer to this question not only determines what a park visitor may do, and what developments are required, but gives the whole concept of preservation meaning and purpose. Can wilderness prevail indefinitely against all of the varied demands of an expanding economy? Yes, when wilderness contributes its proper part in meeting those demands, when the use benefits that flow from its unim-

Mount Olympus glacier carves its way downslope at Olympic National Park, Washington

paired natural scene are sufficient to justify its continuation. The national parks are evidence of this fact.

Wilderness—a Basic Park Resource, an Essential Factor in Park Use

The natural environment is the essential resource of a scenic park or monument, the resource from which appropriate and beneficial enjoyment directly emanates.

This is the law, the tradition, and the philosophy that must guide all planning for each area, whether its distinction lies in a particular feature of scenic or scientific interest or in an expansive wilderness.

The wilderness proper serves all park visitors. Those who penetrate it gain its fullest rewards. But, it is the part of a national park that is not intensively used that makes it a park, and the undeveloped wilderness beyond the roads furnishes the setting and the background. Take away the background, and the park atmosphere of the whole disappears, and with it a very large part of the pleasure of those whose only contact with wilderness is experienced as they look outward over it from the roadside.

Wilderness areas, and the quality of wilderness that must pervade the most visited part of a national park, are a primary resource—a resource to be cherished and guarded, a resource whose benefits each park visitor is entitled to enjoy.

Today, more people than ever before take a personal interest in conservation, national parks, and wilderness. This is easy to understand—it coincides with the phenomenal increase in outdoor recreation and the shrinkage of available open spaces. In the national parks people find something they like, can understand, and want to keep. As an example of conservation in action, national parks have contributed in no small measure to the attitudes and convictions that prevail among the public today.

This favorable circumstance did not always prevail—it is of quite recent origin. During the formative years of national park development, the wilderness beyond the nation's frontiers appeared limitless. Those who could forsee its shrinkage and who proposed to do something about it were generally regarded as alarmists and impractical dreamers. National parks were established through sufferance rather than in response to widespread public demand, and once established, had no ready-made pattern to follow in their management. To a very large degree, the policies and direction of these new areas had to originate with those who administered them.

The process was not without difficulty, nor without error. Problems that are clearly evident now could then be only dimly perceived, and the means to cope with them were largely absent. It took a clear head and a firm hand on their part to start the national parks in the right direction.

Time tends to paint our memory in rosy hues, and we forget how dusty and rough and narrow the first park roads were, that developments for public use were practically nonexistent, and interpretive services completely lacking. Camps were pitched on the most convenient, often the most beautiful sites, and public accommodations were built according to the builders' individual notions, without regard to architectural fitness, landscape values, or long-range planning. Frequently, hotels and camps usurped the most scenic and the most strategic sites in the park. Roadsides sometimes were burned to improve the view, and in Sequoia National Park a colony of private summer homes intruded on the giant forest.

Trespass was common—20,000 sheep had to be driven out of Yosemite one year. Overgrazing during World War I left serious scars on Mount Rainier. Yellowstone's buffalo were brought near to extinction. Hunting trespass was common. Predators were sought out and killed. An early report from Yosemite tells us that any bird or animal unfortunate enough to enter the valley was at once pursued, captured, or killed.

Many parks inherited abused lands, the results of years of misuse and injurious practice. The Kern drainage in Sequoia National Park was so completely denuded by sheep grazing, many years before it was added to the park, that it was hard to find enough forage for a saddle horse. The establishment of Joshua Tree National Monument, Big Bend National Park, and other areas halted depletion of their grasslands.

The last California grizzly was shot in a spot that 20 years later became part of Kings Canyon National Park. The elk were gone from Rocky Mountain National Park and Glacier National Park, the bighorn from Big Bend and Mesa Verde, and the rare birdlife of Everglades National Park was seriously threatened before these areas were established as national parks.

We cite these few examples so that we may avoid the common error of using only the best from the past for comparison with the total picture of today. Generally speaking, conditions have improved greatly through the years —sometimes through the mere circumstance of the establishment of a park, always accompanied by practical acts of management, correction, and protection. Progress along many avenues of park conservation has been steady and sure.

Growth of the National Park System

Since its establishment in 1916 the National Park System has expanded greatly to encompass many kinds of areas—historic, archeologic, and recreational, as well as scenic nature preserves.

Fifteen national parks and eighteen national monuments comprised the National Park System in 1916. By 1956 the National Park Service administered 29 national parks, 84 national monuments, and 69 other kinds of recreational areas. These are primarily areas of scenic-

scientific interest to the American people. Twenty-two of the areas of 1916 were in this category—about 5 million acres. Today, more than 22 million acres—88 percent of all lands administered by the National Park Service—are contained in the 66 scenic-scientific parks, monuments, and other areas.

Except for those transferred to the National Park System, most of the new areas were established after extensive study by the National Park Service, and upon United States Department of the Interior recommendations and representations before Congress. At the same time, numerous proposals for areas found to be of less than national importance have been rejected.

While seeking out needed and suitable areas to complete the National Park System, the National Park Service has maintained the standards of quality that were established in the earlier national parks.

Preservation on the Major Front

Certain laws concerning national park areas prohibit settlement, hunting, mining, and lumbering in them, and similar commercial activities. Where such activities are permitted, Congress has expressly provided for them. The whole body of law is clear in intent, and establishes a firm safeguard against the exploitation of the resources of the national parks for commercial products. Congress reserves to itself the right of final decision on such matters—dams, power development, or pipelines, for example.

Nevertheless, there have been numerous attempts, well organized and powerfully supported, to despoil the national parks of their forests, wildlife, minerals, grasslands, and free-flowing streams. One has to recall Sequoia, Kings Canyon, Glacier, Olympic, Grand Teton, Yellowstone, or Death Valley, to bring some of them to mind.

The National Park Service quite properly assumes the leadership in vigorously

The Yellowstone River cascades over waterfalls in Yellowstone National Park, Wyoming

resisting such invasions. The majority of such attacks are dispelled by the National Park Service and the Department before becoming subjects of public controversy or Congressional action. The more dramatic episodes, however, quickly capture public attention and enlist the defensive efforts of many. Private citizens, numerous organizations, and congressional leaders—all have shared in preserving the integrity of the national parks. There have been a few reversals, but the history of the parks has been one of repeated victories in such contests.

The National Park Service is a public agency. It investigates, plans, and recommends. Frequently it is called upon to harmonize widely divergent interests. Within the scope of its authority, it decides; but in larger issues, matters that go beyond internal park management, it must look to the United States Department of the Interior and to the Congress, reflecting the consensus of the public, for guidance, decision, and direction.

On the broad front, preservation of park and wilderness values depends, therefore, quite as much upon public awareness as it does upon any specific decision that may be made independently by the National Park Service. One of the most encouraging developments over the past 20 years has been the strengthening of conservation education in the public schools—first through the interest of individual teachers, followed by the integration of conservation into the school curriculum. An informed public is the best safeguard of the integrity of the national parks. The cause of wilderness preservation is best advanced when the National Park Service, conservation organizations, and the informed public present a united front on major issues.

Inappropriate Park Use

Some strange proposals find their way to the National Park Service, often suggesting activities completely inappropri-

ate to the best use of the parks. Going back in the files only a few years, for instance, one finds requests for gambling concessions, helicopter sightseeing service, summer theater, pocket billiard concession, miniature golf course, bowling alley, miniature train for sightseeing, cable car into Grand Canyon, gunnery range, lands for farms and summer homes, private airports, as well as requests for stock grazing, lumbering, prospecting, mining, and hundreds more.

The National Park Service immediately rejects such proposals, and it requires no rare understanding of park objectives to make the decisions. Such matters are usually settled within the National Park Service and rarely become subjects of public controversy.

All proposals, however, are not so clear cut, and there is room for many honest differences on some questions of proper park use. Each such case is considered on its own merits in accordance with the following general principles: (1) that the activity result in no impairment of significant natural or scenic values, (2) that it does not itself become a primary attraction, and (3) that it does not lessen the opportunity for others to enjoy the park for what it is.

The rapid increase in park attendance has brought with it ever closer application of the principle of appropriate and beneficial use. The refinement of use standards and close adherence to them are reflected in the very high quality of park use that prevails today.

Private Lands

The existence of privately owned lands within a park is an obstacle to satisfactory management and protection. Adverse use, unsightly developments, and difficult protection and long-range management problems are the result. New areas always add temporarily to the total of such lands within the National Park System. Acquisition, by purchase, donation, or exchange, is a lengthy process, but over the years there has been definite progress.

The 33 areas that comprised the National Park System in 1916 contained well over a million acres of private "inholdings" — more than one-fifth of all lands within the authorized boundaries of that day. By 1956 nearly 90 percent of this land had been acquired leaving less than 150,000 acres within the original 33 areas. Comparable progress has been made in areas added since 1916, but the problem remains a big one, with over 700,000 acres of private lands remaining within the 25 million acres now in the National Park System.

Grazing

It is important not only to hold an area as a national park, and to defend it against threats from without, but also to so order its internal affairs that it does not deteriorate. The problem of grazing will illustrate the point.

Elimination of commercial grazing has been an important goal since the establishment of the National Park Service. In 8 of 11 wilderness parks in the National Park System in 1916, commercial grazing of sheep, cattle, and horses was practiced. Only one of these areas is so used today; more than 64,000 animal grazing months have been eliminated. Comparable gains are evident throughout the National Park System even though the establishment of new areas usually provides that existing grazing privileges be continued for the lifetime of the permittee. The important facts are that, while progress is slow, the ultimate elimination of all grazing has remained the objective, progress is evident, and there has been no regression.

Protection of Plantlife

Over the years, certain basic policies have evolved concerning the maintenance of natural conditions of vegetation. In brief, these are:

Retention of natural forest conditions.
Control of all wildfire; prevention and as complete control as possible of man-caused fires.

Eradication of all exotic pests, and control of epidemic outbreaks of native pests.

Eradication of exotic plants.

Restoration of areas damaged by man-accelerated erosion or depletion of plant cover.

Two aspects of this program have special interest — control of introduced plant diseases, and protection of non-commercial forest tree species.

An old Spanish saying tells us that "All trees are wood, but the pine is not mahogany." In the national parks, all trees *are* "mahogany." Natural and scenic beauty is the justification for forest protection in the national parks; park forests and plant species are regarded as exhibits, as museum specimens, valuable for their natural beauty and their interest as a part of the natural plant association. Many agencies give good protection to commercially valuable forests, but the national parks alone regularly protect noncommercial species of plants from fires, insects, and diseases.

Wildlife

Wildlife, present in variety and in normal abundance, is a major ingredient of wilderness.

Fortunately, many areas were established soon enough, and protection afforded early enough, to preserve animal species that otherwise might have perished; but preservation entails more than the establishment or simple proclamation of a wildlife sanctuary.

The past 50 years have witnessed the elimination of poaching as a factor of consequence; the reversal of the practice of killing predators, the recognition of the place of the predator as a part of a natural fauna; an encouraging degree of recovery of the once endangered trumpeter swan, grizzly bear, bighorn, and bison; the restoration of elk, bison, bighorn, Merriam's turkey, and antelope in some parks from which they had disappeared; and the elimination or partial control of exotic animals in other national parks. Today all forms of native wildlife find sanctuary in the national parks. Most important, the natural environment upon which the wildlife depends has been preserved and restored.

The welfare of park wildlife today and in the future requires much more than the setting aside of adequate range, or protection from injury by man. Limitations of range in even the largest parks, coupled with the continuing pressure of intensive land use in adjacent areas, is perhaps the basic problem; but the relation of man to the native fauna— man using the national parks and traveling into the wilderness in increasing numbers—is also a factor of no mean proportions.

Wildlife in the national parks deserves and will continue to get a full measure of attention. This means continued protection, restoration of species that have disappeared, where possible, and management where required to neutralize the influence of man. It means

The grizzly bear, a rare mammal, is increasing its numbers under National Park protection

*At Big Bend National Park, Texas, the waxy blossoms of Spanish dagger rise
above bayonetlike leaves and short woody trunks*

education, so that people, aware of delicate natural balances, will adjust their behavior and expectations to reality. It means research to reveal the facts upon which a sound program of management, protection, and use must be based.

The wildlife program in the national parks is the only major effort in this country to preserve a complete fauna, in a natural habitat, with minimum disturbance and control.

Interpretation

Education has a great deal to do with man's understanding and enjoyment of wilderness, his wise use and management of it, and his acceptance of the idea of its preservation. The National Park Service recognized this very early and led in the development of an effective interpretive program.

The idea of outdoor nature study in the national parks, tested through trial by a public-minded California couple, Mr. and Mrs. C.M. Goethe, was launched toward its final success in Yosemite in 1920. This program not only has been expanded throughout the areas in the National Park System, but has served as a pattern for similar programs in many state and municipal parks, and other outdoor establishments. Within the national parks in 1956, the interpretive program served more than 26 million visitors at talks, on conducted trips, and in museums and visitor centers. Nearly as many used exhibits and other self-help facilities.

Interpretation gives the visitor a basis for added enjoyment, greater interest and awareness of the natural scene around him, some ideas about conservation, and a clearer idea of his responsibility as a user and protector of the park. The cumulative results over the many years are impressive.

Park Development

Generally speaking, in a national park only those developments are justified that are required in order for visitors to use the park beneficially, and to enjoy and understand the natural scene. This means reasonable access by road and by trail to the area and to selected places within it that will give the visitor a good example of its major qualities. In some parks, it also means campgrounds, accommodations, and other facilities to provide the creature comforts.

Most of the road work of the past 35 years has been reconstruction on or near the location of older roads, bringing the system up to a standard required to handle the travel of the day. In Yellowstone, for example, most of the roads have been rebuilt during the last 40 years, but there have been virtually no new roads into new areas in the past 60 years.

Once reasonable access was provided, there was remarkably little extension of roads in any of the older national parks. In fact, the National Park Service began to pull back on new road construction before it was generally recognized outside the National Park Service that roads—too many of them, or in the wrong places—could impair park and wilderness values.

Roads have been constructed into new areas, and more will be needed, but only to the degree necessary to provide a comparable amount of reasonable access and opportunity in new or in underdeveloped park areas.

Good taste and good judgment are important in the placement and treatment of a park road or developed area, but the practical factors of economics and engineering must be taken into account, too. Some compromise with perfection is unavoidable, but efforts to hold road standards to acceptable limits, to preserve natural conditions along roadsides, to fit park roads to topography while providing scenic and interpretive opportunity, and to achieve appropriateness in design and location of developments, have met with considerable success.

More fundamental, however, is the

overall development and use plan for a park, having to do with road and developed area locations and their integration. Circumstance, rather than a well-controlled plan, controlled the earliest developments in many national parks. Poorly located and ill-planned to start with, their expansion to accommodate mounting travel has created serious problems of overcrowding, impairment of values, and impaired enjoyment. Fortunately, for the first time in the history of the National Park Service, the opportunity to rectify these conditions is now at hand.

Anyone who seeks wilderness can find it in the national parks. It is no problem for those who follow the trails to find solitude, beauty, and adventure far removed from roads and lodges. Even those who never venture far from roads experience the quality of wilderness. For them the wilderness may lie but 10 minutes' walk from most park roads, or they may sense it looking outward from such places as Trail Ridge Road, Going-to-the-Sun Highway, Blue Ridge Parkway, or even from the plaza of Bright Angel Lodge. Whether or not their impression coincides with any definition we may formulate, the visitors see, sense, and react to wilderness, often without leaving the roadside.

This is no accident—it is the result of many years of planned progress along many avenues of park conservation. It reflects discrimination in the selection of superlative scenic, scientific, wilderness areas for inclusion in the National Park System; consistent conformity to the sound concept of use and preservation upon which the national parks are founded; a successful history of resistance to threats of despoilment, impairment, and adverse use; and an internal management program that not only has protected the physical resources but, in many cases, has brought about the recovery of large areas once abused and misused. The growing public awareness of wilderness values, a source of great strength to the conservation movement, is itself in part a product of beneficial use and unimpaired preservation of these areas of great natural beauty.

The wilderness is there; consciously or unconsciously, people respond to it.

Looking to the Future

For the first time in its history the National Park Service has in action a program broad enough to permit effective long-range planning, on a scale large enough to overtake today's problems and to prepare for future ones before they develop. This is Mission 66. It contains nothing new except a broader outlook and the element of scale. It emphasizes a firm determination to carry out without compromise the purpose of national parks as defined by law and strengthened by tradition.

How does the wilderness idea fit into this program?

One may look for the answer in the development plans for roads and developed areas, in plans for the management of the wilderness area proper, and the several separate parts of the Mission 66 program as they pertain to wilderness. But the real answer lies in the precepts that give direction to park planning right from the start, and govern every step of the process.

How does one plan for a national park?

The process required these steps:

Inventory of the significant and distinctive resources of the park or monument. What does the area have?

Evaluation of the human benefits which should derive from those resources. What should people get out of a visit to the area?

Definition of the activities and experiences, the facilities and services required to bring forth those benefits. What must the visitor do, and what must be done for him?

Establishment of controls and limi-

Rocky Mountain National Park, Colorado

tations. To what degree can these things be done without loss of values or impairment of the resource?

The answers to these four questions are the basis for area planning, for they define the area objective, identify the legitimate needs of the visitor, and establish the controls necessary to perpetuate both the resource and the opportunity to enjoy it.

One can apply this line of reasoning, for example, to such areas as Mount Rainier or the Everglades, to Joshua Tree, or Dinosaur, and come up with some fundamental conclusions:

Wilderness — without in any way discounting the value of specific features of high visitor interest such as a geyser or a grove of sequoias — wilderness is the significant resource of such areas.

Every person who visits such areas is entitled to and should have a wilderness experience.

Plans for such areas must preserve large, undeveloped wilderness, and as well the wilderness atmosphere of the park as a whole — the roadsides and the environment of developed areas.

Thus, the guidelines for a park are established, and within them, detailed planning can proceed. With this brief background, one can now look at Mission 66 item by item and understand how each part fits together and contributes, not only to better park use, but to the preservation of natural and wilderness values.

The national parks, to review briefly, are beset by four kinds of problems:

1. Competition for the use of park resources — park recreation versus exploitation for commercial or other public purposes. Today, the national parks are endangered less by the demands of industry for raw materials, than by other forms of public use, such as water and power developments, pipelines, and the like. How such conflicts are resolved depends, as much as any other factor, upon public understanding, and acceptance of the national park objective. Favorable attitudes are generated through beneficial and appropriate park experience. The more a national park is used, profitably and beneficially, for its intended purpose, the less vulnerable are its lands to threats of commercial exploitation.

To prepare the national parks for as full a measure of recreational, educational, inspirational use as they can safely withstand not only is consistent with the park objective, but is also a defense against adverse use. To provide for appropriate and beneficial park use is to safeguard park integrity.

2. Inappropriate or harmful recreational use. Appropriate park use derives from the unimpaired, unmodified, natural scene. There is no place in future plans for activities that deprive any visitor of full enjoyment of the natural scene, or that require unusual or inappropriate facilities or services.

3. Destruction of the physical resources of a park by man-caused or natural agents. The record of progress in protecting park resources from fire, pests, erosion, and the like has been reviewed. Adequate funds, personnel, and facilities will strengthen the protection program all along the line. Equally important, protection will be backed up by continuous observation and research, to better harmonize protection practice, both as to method and degree, with the wilderness principle.

4. Problems attending increased visitation — damage, intrusion, impairment by people and by the facilities they require. This is the basic subject upon which Mission 66 bears most directly, and attacks from several directions.

The Mission 66 plan coordinates all aspects of park operation — management, protection, development, and use. It continues the policies and strengthens the practices of all aspects of park preservation.

As for development, here, too, is a new

opportunity to contribute to preservation while improving the quality of park use. The major contribution of this program to conservation stems from the fact that it *is* comprehensive and long-range. Many of today's problems of congestion, impairment, and incomplete enjoyment were brought on by piecemeal development controlled by expediency and the limitations of the moment. For the first time, it is now possible to plan intelligently to meet future problems, with reasonable assurance that those plans will be carried out. Mission 66 is in a position to use development as a means of better preservation.

There will be no radical departures from past practice in carrying out the details of Mission 66 development. Being a complete and comprehensive plan, does, however, give new emphasis and new force to certain aspects of it.

Park Roads

Only two things about the Mission 66 program need be said: (1) Roads will not be extended into any area now considered park wilderness; the rebuilding of existing roads to bring them to a standard required today, and the completion of roads on a comparable scale in newer areas, constitute most of the road construction program; (2) the road system for a park is considered to be a basic instrument of park presentation and interpretation, and this principle will influence future road plans.

Developed Areas

The most significant scenic, scientific, or historical areas within a park shall be reserved exclusively for esthetic, interpretive, and recreational enjoyment. Other developments — accommodations and administrative facilities—when they are necessary in a park, shall be restricted, and if necessary, relocated, in the less scenic and less vital portions of the parks. This is the principle behind the development of Colter Bay in Grand Teton, for example; the New Canyon Village to replace intrusive facilities now on the rim of Yellowstone Canyon; the proposal to move the headquarters for Mount Rainier out of the park; to transfer developments from Spruce Tree Point to a less vital area in Mesa Verde; to limit accommodations in Everglades; to eliminate accommodations in Rocky Mountain; and to limit public use development in Yosemite Valley and to transfer all possible administrative and utility facilities outside that park.

This is the direction in which the National Park Service will move in future planning for other areas, but it will take longer than the lifetime of Mission 66 to complete the job. The pattern is set, and the way is clear to save the most precious areas and features for the purpose for which they are best suited— refreshment of the body, mind, and spirit.

The Wilderness Proper

Almost every problem and every principle discussed has counterparts in the problems of use and preservation of those extensive, undeveloped, natural areas we call wilderness. The wilderness, too, will be used by people—not intensively, for remoteness and the difficulty of travel and subsistence will remain a relatively effective safeguard against mass use. Nevertheless, use by people is recognized whenever we evaluate wilderness in terms of human experience—solitude, remoteness, quietude, beauty, sense of adventure.

Wilderness areas are most enjoyed by those who penetrate them. But, they also benefit every person who travels through a park. It is the undeveloped wild land beyond the roads that provide the setting and the background. Wilderness areas are preserved, not alone for the hiker, but equally for the benefit of all.

Wilderness areas are preserved by excluding roads, and developments for permanent occupancy and by leaving the natural resources unexploited. All of this is inherent in the Mission 66 program, but to stop at this point would be

Black Mountain fire tower stands guard over a New Hampshire forest

an oversimplification of the problem. Wilderness, as it exists today, cannot long endure without attention—let us call it management, by which we mean only this: to correct and neutralize the influence of man. It does not mean control of natural forces or management of the environment for the purpose of creating a better wilderness.

As a consequence, the National Park Service extinguishes fires in the wilderness, controls pests and diseases, and repairs damage resulting from man's activities. Trails are provided—to permit access and legitimate use, but also to minimize and localize the impact of feet and hoofs. When the number of wilderness users becomes significant the National Park Service may, justifiably, prepare sites for camps, or for campfires, and arrange for the disposal of refuse to minimize and localize the effects of use. Regulation may be needed —limiting numbers, length of stay, the

man-to-horse ratio, fishing, or other recreation practices. Each wilderness area is a special case, and any combination of these or other management practices may be called for to minimize the effects of man's presence.

Wilderness areas must be protected as well from impairment resulting from conditions existing outside their boundaries. Park streams whose headwaters drain from disturbed lands become silted; wildlife problems are created in the parks because of predator control and the like beyond their borders; and epidemic insect infestations are generated in nearby burns or logging operations. These are but a few of many examples that might be cited.

Wilderness today is but a fragment of the wilderness that was. Wilderness has been reduced and divided; this, too, is man's doing, much of it inescapable.

When wilderness spanned the continent, wildfire, insects, and diseases were natural, normal factors in its ecology. The result was a varied environment, comprised of many plant types, many overlapping generations and stages of succession.

Today, wildfire, and insect and disease infestations still occur, but now they have the capacity to change a much reduced wilderness area to a one-stage condition. It is the purpose of the Nationl Park Service to preserve a true sample of wilderness. This requires that natural forces be regulated to the degree necessary to keep them in scale with the reduced size of the wilderness that remains today.

Better Use of the Whole Park

Mission 66 seeks to make those parts of a park that are already developed more effective in meeting visitor needs for refreshment, enjoyment, understanding, and inspiration. To move accommodations to less vital places is one step in the direction of dispersal of use. But more is planned.

Park roads will be utilized as an interpretive device, with roadside exhibits, markers, and signs as required. A journey through a park will become a continuous experience in seeing, understanding, and appreciating the natural scene, with many places for the visitor to pause for a spectacular view, to see a roadside exhibit, to walk a park trail. The objective of all is threefold: to relieve the impact of multiple use of the climax scenic areas, to make more of the park usable, interesting, and enjoyable, and to emphasize the natural scene as the true climax element of a park experience.

Presentation and Interpretation

To present and interpret a park in its most meaningful, most interesting, and most attractive light is the key idea behind all planning for visitor use, and to a very great degree it determines what developments and what services visitors require. The ultimate National Park System will provide a full representation of America — its scenic lands and natural features, and its history. It goes a long way toward doing so now. It is most important for that scene and that history to be so presented and so interpreted that it will have full meaning for Americans. To understand and appreciate wilderness is the first step in its preservation.

Research

Mission 66 proposes a much strengthened program of research and observation. Increased park use has introduced an element that year by year renders the problems of protection and preservation of the natural scene more complex. The normal pace of nature is slow, and the influence of man upon an environment is often indirect, obscure, and delayed, and often not recognized in time to take preventive action. National park use, management, and protection practices must be guided by accurate knowledge, secured through continuous observation and study of the natural scene and of man's effect upon it. This portion of Mission 66, although small, is extremely important, Guesswork, rule-of-thumb, and intuition are not good enough — the preservation of this irreplacable resource requires precise knowledge and scientific procedure.

A Recreation Plan for America

In 1936 the National Park Service started a study of the recreational needs, and an inventory of the potential recreation areas, of the United States. Interrupted by the war, this study is again under way as a part of Mission 66. Already a survey of the Atlantic and Gulf coasts is completed, and studies of the Pacific Coast and Great Lake regions have started. The object of the National Recreation Plan is to point the way, and to stimulate the establishment of outdoor recreation areas by all governments — federal, state and municipal.

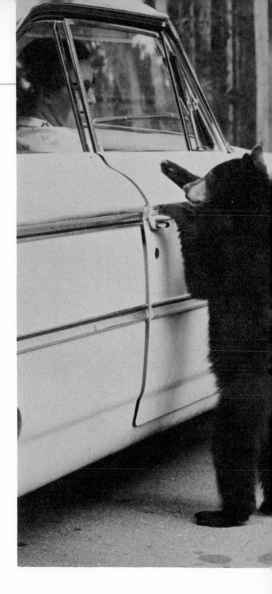

What has this to do with parks?

This, for one thing: When enough other outdoor areas are developed to serve the growing need for recreation, pressure to expand developments and extend roads in the national parks will diminish.

Leisure time is rapidly expanding, much more rapidly than the nation is providing for in its worthwhile use. There is no time to lose if the people of the states and of the nation are to retain seashores and mountains, forests, rivers, and lakes for their own refreshment and enjoyment. The good use of leisure — use that will strengthen the moral fiber of America—is a responsibility of every type of government. To provide leadership in this direction is the real objective of this program.

The national parks were established in an atmosphere of high idealism. The men gathered around that wilderness campfire in the Yellowstone the evening of September 19, 1870, started the first major conservation movement in the United States. It was an act of unselfish citizenship that has become an American guidepost to the world in conservation.

It is now 95 years since the idea of national parks became a reality, and was clearly defined by law. Today, it is fair to claim that nine-tenths of the area within the national parks can be included under a reasonable definition of wilderness, that the admonition to preserve for the benefit of the people and to pass on unimpaired to future generations has been faithfully carried out.

For the future, one can take assurance from the tradition of national park conservation and the laws that give it strength, from the record of protective management, from the dedication of an alert and loyal group of park employees, from the devotion to the cause of an evergrowing body of citizens, and from the promise of Mission 66.

The national parks occupy an incomparable position among the scenic wonders of the world. Americans have inherited a collection of masterpieces. With that heritage is this obligation: to conserve the nation's scenic and historic treasures, and to prepare the areas of the National Park System for their task—the enjoyment and inspiration of this and future generations.   —H.R.S.

Do Not Feed the Bears

There is no doubt about it—most visitors to the magnificent national parks of America find the bears one of the chief attractions. Neither is there any doubt that those who keep the greatest distance between themselves and the four-footed objects of their admiration and interest are the wisest.

The black bear, though seemingly friendly, is a wild animal

For bears, despite their sometimes deceptively friendly, even playful, manner, are wild animals of great strength, and therefore dangerous (*See under Bear*).

It is of the black bear that this is written, as the grizzly is seldom seen by visitors. The black bear, which may also be varying shades of brown and even yellowish, is native to most of the United States and is, consequently, well represented in nearly all the national parks. These parks, owing to their natural beauty and the release they afford people from humdrum work and the tensions of modern living, are attracting more and more vacationers each year. The ingredients for trouble, however, are present, and each year a considerable number of both visitors and bears are the worse for having been a part of it.

One example, a little extreme, perhaps, but by no means an isolated case occurred in the Great Smoky Mountains National Park of North Carolina and Tennessee in the summer of 1954. A ranger, driving through the park one day happened upon a parked car, the right front seat of which was occupied by a woman. Standing at the open left front door was a full grown bear and behind him a man doing his urgent best to push the bear into the automobile! Stopping his car, the ranger leaped out, bear stick in hand. Calling to the man to step aside, he threatened the bear with the stick, whereupon it lumbered off into the woods. The man, when bluntly confronted by the ranger, explained that he had only been trying to push the bear into the driver's seat to obtain a snapshot of his wife—with the bear ostensibly driving the car—beside her! On another occasion an Ohio farmer was caught in the act of trying to rope a bear. As punishment he was required to distribute 150 bear-warning leaflets to other visitors.

There are an estimated 300 black bears in the Great Smoky National Park. This park, due to its location near heavily populated areas and the great beauty of its half-a-million acres, annually attracts more people than any other national park. Most of the visitors long for at least a glimpse of a wild bear. More than that, many of them are determined to secure, by hook or by crook, a *picture* of a wild bear. Thus, in spite of warning leaflets and conspicuously posted signs reading in effect: "Please do not feed or in any way molest the bears—they are dangerous wild animals," numerous tourists are roughed up, scratched, and clawed each year because they persist in regarding bears as cuddly playthings.

A bear, understandably, loses his taste for ground squirrels, roots, mice, frogs, and berries after he acquires a liking for such man-made delicacies as sandwiches, canned goods, hot dogs, popcorn, and candy bars. In addition to becoming a gourmet he may, in a small way, become an amateur psychologist. Having learned that humans are apt to

The black bear varies in color from black to brown, yellow, cinnamon, and even bluish

have flavorful provisions in their pockets or in a paper bag, he approaches them with a sad expression on his muzzle, rises on his hind legs, perhaps extends a paw for good measure, and throws in a little clowning. This seldom fails to elicit at least a cookie or a nibble of cake, which is quickly dispatched by the bear which then plainly expects more of the same. This he receives—and gulps.

The routine continues until the donor decides either that enough is enough or since things are going so well he will play with this harmless fellow a bit. Either way he may be in for trouble. If, for example, he playfully snatches the food away just as the bear is about to take it, he is lucky if he merely loses the sleeve of his coat. If the bear's sensitive nose informs him that the car contains more of the goodies he has just been denied he is not averse to tearing off the cardoor in order to secure them. Some bears have taken to living along the highway and begging their keep from the tourists. The inevitable result of this is the degradation of the bear from the status of a wild animal worthy of respect to that of a roadside beggar.

Unquestionably there are among bears, as among all other large species of wild animals, certain individuals that would, under any circumstances, be dangerous to man. Generally, however, when a bear has to be killed it is because he is the victim of clouded perception on the part of the human beings with whom he has been in contact.

When, for instance, a bear is seen near a highway in the Smokies a traffic block known as a "bear jam" nearly always ensues. Although the persons involved would make for the closest shelter at top speed were they to encounter a bear at home, there, strangely enough, they conclude the bear must be tame. They stop their cars, jump out, and run toward the bear, meanwhile busily adjusting their cameras. Soon a circle of enthusiastic and curious persons surrounds the bear which, feeling

In the wild, black bears avoid man

hemmed in, gets panicky and charges out of the circle—cuffing or clawing the unlucky persons who get in its way. On weekends these "bear jams" become large and noisy, with tourists shouting and blowing automobile horns. Occasionally, in the general excitement, a driver may fail to set the brakes and his car careens down the mountainside while he watches the bear.

Each year in the many parks that are a natural habitat for bears some have to be killed. In one especially bad year at Yellowstone, 50 bears were executed. That year 115 persons were injured by bears. Sometimes bears that have been corrupted by contact with humanity are live-trapped and transported to points in the park far distant from the point where viciousness was shown. Some remain there to live naturally. Most, however, seem to find their way back to the highways and the open-handed tourist living. This, unfortunately, underlines the failure of the public to understand one basic principle of the national park system. The wildlife within the parks is there because it is native to the area. If the bears were not wild they would have no place within park boundaries. Being there, the primitive law of the survival of the fittest prevails. The bear whose tastes and character have been degenerated by contact with man may become a nuisance, or even a menace. Through no fault of its own, it may no longer be acceptable in the national parks.

It is to be hoped that the visiting millions will soon become aware of the damage their failure to read and heed the park service warnings is doing; that they will come more and more to regard themselves as trustees of these primeval parks and all they contain — parks dedicated to their natural complement of wild things, and to the fullest enjoyment of the people.   —C.E.

Threats to National Parks and National Monuments

Threats to the areas of the National Park System invariably arise from efforts to claim some economic advantage, the benefits of which would accrue to a locality or private groups. The fact that all the people of the nation have a stake in the parks and monuments is apt to be disregarded. Pressure generated by local groups can be rapidly applied, but it takes time for the realization of the danger to reach the numerous but widely scattered individuals and organizations interested in the national parks and for them to make known their opposition.

Fortunately, such effective and well-known organizations as the National Audubon Society can, and frequently do, come to the rescue in helping to forestall a particular threat. But it is going to require constant support of a definite and positive park conservation program if America is to preserve the scenic, scientific, and wilderness resources the Congress of the United States has already set aside. As the national economy finds use for more hydroelectric power, timber, minerals, and agricultural and grazing lands, so will pressure groups increase their efforts to invade the parks. Proposals to take park lands are usually not made for areas that are well known to the public. They are usually made concerning areas which the public, by and large, has not had an opportunity to see. There is little doubt that the people of the United States lost Hetch Hetchy Valley in Yosemite National Park many years ago simply because the public did not realize then that Hetch Hetchy was a second Yosemite Valley and that within a few years it would have become of incalculable value for public inspiration and enjoyment. Even a third-rate access road, campgrounds, and sanitary facilities in Hetch Hetchy, had they been available at that time, might have saved the valley for park use. But too few people had seen the valley at the time its use for a reservoir was proposed, and the reservoir proposal won out.

There is need, therefore, for conservationists everywhere to adopt a positive approach to the whole park conservation program now, rather than to wait until a threat appears. A positive approach means the building of a common front against the thought that qualified and duly established national parks and monuments, because the land is owned by the people, or because they have inviting dam sites or grazing or timber producing potentialities, should be considered for exploitation unless the very welfare of the nation should depend upon it. A positive approach means the

The exploitation of natural resources and the need for more grazing lands poses a serious threat to the welfare of the national parks

building in the minds of the public a real understanding of the conservation of natural resources for human use and enjoyment. It should start in the schools where, at the present time, conservation of American natural resources is spoken of in terms of board feet, tons, and kilowatt hours. A positive approach means that, consistent with the nation's fiscal and other responsibilities, people must continually work to maintain and to develop the national parks and monuments to a reasonable extent, especially the new and less-known areas, in order that they may be enjoyed by people in the manner intended. Otherwise, they will be plucked off one by one for other uses.

Katmai and Glacier Bay National Monuments in Alaska, Olympic in Washington, Kings Canyon in California, Grand Teton in Wyoming, Big Bend in Texas, Everglades in Florida, and many other national parks and monuments have been criticized because of their lack of accessibility and use. It is believed that the preservation of these areas would be much more secure and that they would be more nearly serving their intended purpose if they could be seen and enjoyed by more people. This does not mean that roads have to be built into wilderness. But it does mean more campgrounds, trails, boating, and other services to make backcountry use of the parks more feasible.

Some of the most serious threats to the National Park System come from the demands for water impoundments—proposals to build hydroelectric and flood control structures within the parks and monuments.

Fortunately, the original Federal Power Act was amended to preclude the commission from granting licenses for the construction of dams by private concerns in the areas of the National Park System, but in a few instances, park laws were so written as to provide a certain degree of vulnerability because of recognition of federal projects for dams and reservoirs that were under way or seriously contemplated when the areas were set aside. Such is the case at Grand Canyon, Glacier, Rocky Mountain, and Lassen Volcanic. For Grand Canyon the provision is so worded as to give a measure of discretion to the Secretary of the Interior to oppose project proposals that would be inconsistent with the primary purposes of the park.

In those few cases where there are dams and reservoirs in the parks, such as Hetch Hetchy and Lake Eleanor in Yosemite, Jackson Lake in Grand Teton, minor impoundments in Olympic and the privately owned power dam in Sequoia, the projects existed either before establishment of the National Park Service or of the individual parks. The authority to construct reclamation reservoirs in Glacier National Park was granted by the Congress to make possible certain minor water storage projects for the benefit of the Blackfoot Indians contemplated at the time the park was established.

Coming now to the problem of protecting park forest resources, it has always seemed to some people that the United States is wastefully locking up timber by not permitting logging. It is difficult to convince these individuals that, for inspirational purposes, the maintenance of a superlative virgin forest is absolutely essential. Second-growth timber is *not* as inspiring as the great trees of a primeval forest. Moreover, once logging is introduced, no matter how selective or restrictive it may be, the forest ecology is changed and the area, as a nature museum of scientific interest, is impaired. Conservationists are all familiar with the repeated proposals to eliminate the finest portions of the rain forest from Olympic National Park. Some demands for a reduction of the park boundaries resulted in the appointment by the Governor of the State of Washington of a commission to study the matter. There also were hearings in the State of Washington by a subcommittee of the House Interior and Insular Affairs Committee.

With reference to grazing, the National Park Organic Act authorizes the Secretary of the Interior to "grant the privilege to graze livestock within any national park, monument, or reservation . . . when in his judgment such use is not detrimental to the primary purpose for which such park, monument, or reservation was created." The United States Department of the Interior has long held that the grazing of domestic livestock is incompatible with the preservation of natural conditions. Most of the grazing problems within the national parks were inherited when the lands involved were transferred from the national forests or public domain or, as in the case of Badlands National Monument, where grazing was authorized as an emergency measure in wartime. The reduction and eventual elimination of livestock grazing from the national parks and monuments is an important objective of the Service, but, in all fairness to the individuals whose livestock is affected, it will have to be accomplished gradually and in some cases over a considerable period of time.

With the exception of Mt. McKinley where the act establishing the park provides for continuing the mining laws in effect, mining is not permitted in the national parks. Three monuments, however—Glacier-Bay, Death Valley, and Organ Pipe Cactus—have statutory provision to allow mining with surface uses subject to regulation by the Secretary of the Interior. It is gratifying that there has been relatively little mining activity in any of these areas.

In Everglades National Park, Florida, in order to effect its establishment, it was necessary to acquire some lands with outstanding oil, gas, and mineral rights and leases. Also, the area of Joshua Tree National Monument, California, was reduced in 1950 to eliminate known areas chiefly valuable for mining. Although careful surveys indicated that the remainder contains little significant mineral values, certain interests continue to press for opening the monument to mining. And in recent years the search for uranium-bearing ores has led to requests by the Atomic Energy Commission to make surface reconnaissance studies in certain areas of the National Park System. With the exception of Capitol Reef National Monument, however, this activity has been confined to permission for exploration with Geiger counters and scintillators.

These are a few examples that illustrate the kinds of threats that would surely result in the eventual destruction of the National Park System unless they are successfully resisted or otherwise avoided.

The defense against specific threats, to be successful, usually requires the concerted efforts of conservationists throughout the country. Few among the millions of annual visitors to the areas of the National Park System would willingly consent to destruction of the values for which those areas were set apart.

The National Park Service program strives to impart a background of park philosophy and park objectives as well as a knowledge of natural history or history to the visitor in the national parks. Having had presented to him the facts of natural history and history of the areas he visits, and their relation to the use and conservation objectives of the parks and monuments, the average visitor acquired deeper, more satisfying understanding of the areas of which he is a part owner. This not only fits him better to avoid damaging an area during his visit but also better equips him to evaluate and resist proposals for unwarranted encroachment. The volume of mail that the National Park Service received with regard to the Dinosaur and Olympic threats were ample evidence of this.

Although individual support and interest is a great help in protecting the

National parks provide campsites for millions of American campers

national parks from encroachment for commercial exploitation and private gain, the most effective and powerful support comes from large conservation organizations such as the National Audubon Society. An organized group can speak for many. The defense of the National Park Service against proposed encroachments has been enormously aided in this manner. The best defense is offense; the best defense against undesirable and damaging encroachments upon the National Park System is the continuous and enlightened support of a definite and positive park conservation program.

As most people know, the American system of democracy works through a representative form of government. If the millions of conservation-minded citizens of the country are interested in having their national parks and monuments more adequately protected and made more accessible for public use, their representatives in Congress, who make the appropriations and establish basic policies, will want to know that. They will also want to know if the National Park Service is doing a good job. If park visitors are interested in having better interpretive programs, more wildlife research, better camping grounds, more adequate ranger service, and more adequate accommodations, not only do the Secretary of the Interior and his staff want to know this but the representatives in Congress will want to know it also.

Nationwide organizations such as the National Audubon Society are especially effective, both as a means of keeping the public informed on matters of conservation, and in speaking for the public when conservation projects and programs are at stake. While it is recognized that there always will be times when emergency defense actions must be taken, an interest in these should not be permitted to obscure the more fundamental importance of supporting year in and year out a definite and positive national park conservation program. —C.W.

NATIONAL WILDLIFE REFUGES

The approximately 300 national wildlife refuges in the United States are under the administration of the Bureau of Sport Fisheries and Wildlife, one of the divisions of the Fish and Wildlife Service of the United States Department of the Interior. National parks generally offer scenery, recreation, and glimpses of wildlife to the public, whereas the national wildlife refuges provided protection, often vitally needed, to certain species of birds or mammals (*See National Parks and National Monuments*). The public is encouraged to visit our national parks; the national refuges are often difficult of access. Entry to them is usually prohibited without permission, which may not be granted during the wildlife breeding and nesting season or at other times when visitation might endanger certain species that live within the refuges.

The creation of the refuges has played a major part in the continued existence of some threatened species of wildlife (*see Extinct and Threatened Animals of North America*) and is one of the greatest factors in the maintenance of the large populations of others. Without the refuges, the American bison, the fur seal, the Key deer, the California condor, the whooping crane, and the sooty and noddy terns would have been exterminated in the wild state, or reduced to a few individuals whose extinction would be only a matter of time.

The refuges also serve as sanctuaries for hunted species, including the continent's ducks, geese, and waterfowl, where protection of breeding areas, stopover points along the flyways, and wintering grounds, provide the only means whereby survivors of the annual shotgun barrage can live to reproduce their kind.

The largest of the refuges is Aleutian Islands Wildlife Refuge, 1,200 miles in length and containing 4,250 square miles. The nearly extinct sea otter is there increasing its numbers. The Alaskan brown bear, the blue fox, and the bearded seal also inhabit the lonely, foggy islands. Emperor geese, Steller's eider, and many other waterfowl are found there, but the tremendous numbers of seabirds—puffins, murrelets, and auklets—provide the greatest interest for visitors to the refuge.

The largest race of moose is the Kenai, on the peninsula of the same name on the southern coast of Alaska. The Kenai National Moose Range contains 3,214 square miles, and contains Dall sheep, mountain goats, and wolves.

One of the most famous of all the wildlife refuges is Aransas National Wildlife Refuge, because this marshy region on the Texas coast is the wintering grounds of the last of the whooping cranes. A massive campaign by conservationists has made the plight of North America's largest wader known to the world (*See under Crane*). With the protection given it by Canada in the region where it nests, by the United States in its winter home, and by both countries along its migration route, the world population of whoopers in the wild reached 41 in 1964, an increase of about 10 from the low point of several years earlier. In complete contrast to Aransas are the three national wildlife refuges for the desert bighorn—the Desert, Kofa, and Cabeza Prieta game ranges, totalling 5,484 square miles of arid country in Nevada and Arizona. Mountain ranges there are crowned with conifers, their slopes clothed with hardwoods, and the wide valley floors are wild cactus gardens.

Bison, once nearly exterminated, roam the National Bison Range in Montana and the Wichita Mountains Wildlife Refuge in Oklahoma (*See under Bison*). The National Elk Refuge is in Jackson Hole, Wyoming; elk occur in other refuges and in national parks, but are in greatest numbers within the refuge.

The pronghorn, once resident over much of the open country of the West, is still numerous on the Hart Mountain National Antelope Refuge, in south-central Oregon. A plateau covered with sagebrush, it forms a good summer range for the animals, and is not far from the Sheldon Antelope Range and the Sheldon Antelope Refuge, both in Nevada.

Refuges established primarily for waterfowl are numerous. Along the Pacific Flyway, Malheur (Oregon), Red Rock Lakes (Montana), Bear River (Utah), Lower Klamath, Tule Lake and Sacramento (California) carry tremendous populations of geese and ducks, with the once almost extinct trumpeter swans as the main attraction at Red Rock Lakes.

Lower Souris, Upper Souris, and Des Lacs wildlife refuges, in North Dakota, are important breeding grounds for many species of ducks, and a stopover point for others that breed in northern Canada. Reelfoot National Wildlife Refuge in Tennessee, and White River, in Arkansas, lie on the Mississippi waterfowl flyway.

Along the eastern seaboard, Susquehanna Wildlife Refuge (Maryland) offers a haven to diving and dabbling ducks and whistling swans, which, in their southward flight to wintering areas, can pass on to the safety of Blackwater (Maryland), Chincoteague (Virginia), to Swanquarter and Mattamuskeet (North Carolina), and to Santee, Cape Romain, and Savannah River (South Carolina). Some of the waterfowl stay in the Carolinas, others continue south to Loxahatchee or St. Marks National Wildlife Refuge in Florida, or to Lacassine and Sabine on the Louisiana coast, or Laguna Atascosa, or Aransas in Texas.

Some wildlife refuges were established to protect one species. Moosehorn, in Maine, is a woodcock breeding area. The Great White Heron National Wildlife Refuge, in the Florida Keys, protects this large, pure white heron that rarely leaves mangrove-studded Florida Bay. Pelican Island, on Florida's east coast, is a huge rookery of these ungainly birds, and holds the distinction of being the first federal wildlife refuge; it was

White pelicans

Many animals that are eagerly sought by hunters find safety in the wildlife refuges. Elk(right), pronghorn, or antelope, and Canada geese are among them

created in 1903 by President Roosevelt.

Wherever they are located, the wild-life refuges become havens for many species of birds and other animals, also for interesting or unusual trees and wild-flowers. The ban on hunting and trap-ping, and the management that insures adequate food for residents and migrants alike, favor the natural increase of all wild things. In some of the refuges the unhurried throngs of bison or elk, the clouds of migrating waterfowl, or the busy community of the beaver pond, all bring back a picture of an older America, one that almost vanished under the ex-ploitation of the last two hundred years. Far more than a few birds and mammals have been preserved in our national wildlife refuges. (*See also Okefenokee; Souris*)

—G.B.S.

NATURE CENTER

What is a Nature Center?

A nature center is, in essence, an outdoor focal point where the citizens of a community, both young and old, can enjoy a segment of the natural world and learn something about the interrelationship of living and nonliving things, including man's place in the ecological community. Thus conceived, a dynamic nature center provides innumerable educational, scientific, cultural, and recreational benefits to the community, values that are far-reaching locally, where the sinews of our free society are built.

The nature center is a fairly new concept in community education and recreation and as such should not be confused with nature schools or nature museums.

A nature center is not, for example, a park. A park is known for many of its man-made recreational facilities and often contains animals and plants not native to the area. Some parklands can be set aside as natural areas, however, and when properly developed for educational use can very well become nature centers.

A nature center is not a zoo. A zoo specializes in exhibiting caged animals, native and those from foreign lands. A nature center specializes in displaying local native animals, plants, and geological features as they are actually seen in nature.

A nature center is not a museum, although it may incorporate some of the features of a museum such as a natural science building with exhibits. A museum houses inanimate materials mostly in a state of preservation. A nature center emphasizes the exhibition of living and nonliving things in their natural state out of doors.

A nature center is not a community forest *per se,* that is, managed for watershed protection and forest management by and for the community. Again, however, it may incorporate some of these desirable features, but the purpose and uses are different. A nature center is for educational, scientific, cultural, and recreational use and includes as varied a terrain and landscape as possible—woods, fields, meadows, swamps, marshes, streams, shorelines, and so on.

The ideal nature center, then, is a representative sample of the natural landscape of a community, whatever the local environment may be, such as forest, prairie, tidelands, hill country—a part of wild America set aside and interpreted for the enjoyment and edification of the people of a community. It is designed to teach the community ecological realities and in this way to help its citizens plan their uses of the land scientifically and responsibly.

Value of a Nature Center

One of the real values a center provides is a sense of breathing space for the city. By providing a buffer strip of open land between housing and industrial developments, the area occupied by the center performs a valuable hinterland function in the *open space* plan of communities.

Secondly, a nature center is valuable because it provides an opportunity for local people to help themselves in outdoor education and recreation. It stimulates individual and group community initiative, pride, responsibility, and work, which are the basis of much of what we hold dear in a democratic society.

Most important, a nature center provides an effective learning situation where experiences are direct and people can learn by doing and working. At a nature center, the out-of-doors is real. It is replete with excitement, exploration, and adventure. It is filled with wonderful work opportunities for youngsters. Moreover, learning is rapid and easy because the learner is stimulated and has fun.

Learning is not the sole reason, however, why a nature center is valuable to a community, important as nature edu-

A nature trail at Columbus, Ohio, features an improved walkway

cation and conservation understanding may be. There are other significant values. One is the opportunity that a nature center affords people in such things as esthetic enjoyment and spiritual refreshment. "Everybody," John Muir, an early American conservationist, once said, "needs beauty as well as bread, places to play in and pray in, where nature may heal and cheer, and give strength to body and soul." (*See National Parks*)

Elements of a Nature Center

A nature center includes three basic elements: *land, buildings, and people.*

The land element is basic. Without it there is no nature center. The area should be large enough to meet immediate and future needs of the community, and it should be as undeveloped and varied as possible.

Undeveloped parcels of native land are hard to come by, especially in urban areas, and those that remain are disappearing rapidly. This is why the securing of land, in as generous an amount as possible, should take number one priority in a community considering a nature center.

The land need not be so-called virgin

Many species of cacti can be viewed at the Sonora Desert Museum, Arizona

country. But it should be undeveloped and contain as much native plant and animal life of the local area as can be had. It should be, in a simple sense, a sample of the native landscape of the area. In the eastern United States a typical nature center by all means should have some native woods and, where possible, such added habitat as fields, meadows, marshes, swamps, bogs, streams, and riverbanks and pond, lake or marine shoreline. Few communities, it is true, will have all these features,

but many will have some or a majority of them.

In the arid or semiarid West, communities may have to settle for a dry-plains area without trees or simply a section of unspoiled desert, with its native animals, plants, and geologic features.

How much land should a nature center contain? This is hard to specify, because communities vary in size, and conditions of land availability are different. Certainly 50 acres should be close to a

Ponds at Bernheim Forest, Clermont, Kentucky, abound with water lilies

minimum, with 100 to 300 acres much more suitable. Even 2,000 to 3,000 acres is not too large an area. The smaller the site, the fewer animals it will contain, since each species must satisfy a wide range of requirements. Where possible the land should be in one tract, although several parcels of land near each other should not be ruled out.

The second important element of a nature center is buildings. To run a nature center effectively one must have a place where people can meet. An education building, then, with an orientation-assembly room, exhibits, displays, bookstore, offices, rest rooms, and a workshop, is essential. Not only should visitors have a place where they can be properly briefed on the area, but appropriate shelter must be available during bad weather so that visitors may remain in the nature center if they wish to.

The central education building should be large enough to include, if possible,

a museum wing; thus, a separate natural history museum can be erected and properly equipped with interpretive material

In addition to the education building and museum, the center may have one or more residences or cottages for the staff. Admittedly the staff does not have to live on the premises; however, certain advantages of supervision and control are obtained by this arrangement.

The third and final element necessary in a true nature center is, of course, people. Two groups are involved here: the administrative and operational staff of the center itself, and the visitors who come to the center to learn and understand and enjoy what the center has to offer.

The staff of a typical nature center should have a trained educational director, one or two professional assistants to help with the instruction, a clerk-stenographer, and a caretaker. The director and his teaching staff should

Nature centers such as rustic Glen Helen at Yellow Springs, Ohio (above), and this modern center at Everglades, Florida (below), provide facilities for people interested in nature

The nature center at Kalamazoo, Michigan, features a circular meeting hall with a glass dome roof

be professionally trained in the natural sciences and conservation and skilled as instructors of both young and old. They must have the respect and confidence of the community.

The nature center will attract people of all ages, both as individuals and in groups. There will be those who will want to make solitary sojourns into the area for the pure joy of a walk in the woods or simply to admire the beauty of the natural objects present. In time there will be groups — school classes with their teachers, to learn something of natural history and conservation; toddler groups with the mothers out strolling by themselves; groups of the physically and mentally handicapped, some in wheel chairs, moving along on special trails designed for them. Finally, there will be adult group leaders — counsellors, teachers, and civic and youth group leaders — who will want to come for more specialized instruction in natural history and conservation, including methods of presenting subject matter.

Certain facilities are needed for the comfort and convenience of visitors. An education center with adequate assembly rooms, exhibit halls, and rest rooms

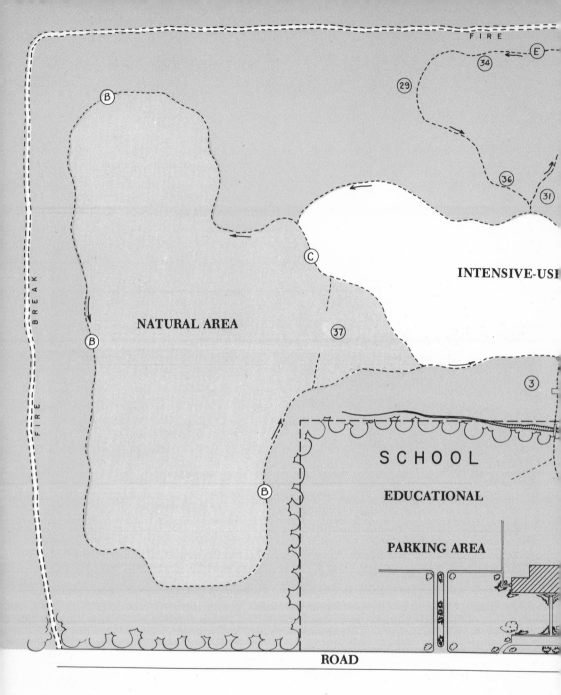

FIRE

E

34

29

36

31

B

C

INTENSIVE-US[

NATURAL AREA

3

B

37

B

S C H O O L

EDUCATIONAL

FIRE BREAK

B

PARKING AREA

ROAD

A SUGGESTED LAYOUT FO

A community nature center should have a *natural area* that is not developed
except for simple foot-trails. This area should comprise one-third to one-half of the
nature center land. A *management area* should be included where the best conservation practices for soil, water, forests, and wildlife can be demonstrated. An
educational area should be developed where visitors can meet at a nature center
building. Adequate parking space should be made available. The *intensive-use
area* should be easily accessible from the educational area. Here, nature center
visitors can be instructed in projects connected with classroom teaching at the
nature center building.

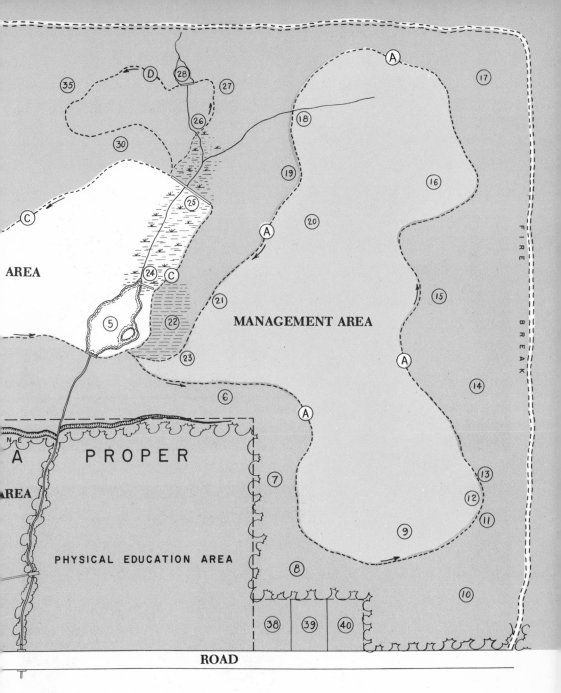

COMMUNITY NATURE CENTER

A. MANAGEMENT TRAIL
B. HIKING TRAIL
C. GENERAL CONSERVATION TRAIL
D. WILDLIFE TRAIL
E. SOIL & GEOLOGY TRAIL
1. ENTRANCE SIGN
2. SHELTER
3. WEATHER STATION

4. COUNCIL RING
5. POND & ISLAND
6. FOREST PRODUCTS DISPLAY
7. THINNING DEMONSTRATION
8. SELECTIVE CUT DEMONSTRATION
9. MANAGED HARDWOOD FOREST
10. CHRISTMAS TREE PLANTATION

11. TREE STUMP & LOG
12. BEE TREE
13. DEN TREE
14. OPENINGS FOR WILDLIFE
15. SHELTWOOD CUT- DEMONSTRATION
16. MANAGED SUGAR BUSH
17. MANAGED MIXED FOREST
18. WATERSHED MANAGEMENT
19. FOREST SOILS STUDY
20. NATURAL SUCCESSION
21. FIRE PREVENTION STORY
22. WILDLIFE PLANTINGS
23. FIRE FIGHTING TOOL DISPLAY BOX
24. TEACHING PLATFORM
25. WALKWAY OVER MARSH

26. STREAM IMPROVEMENT
27. PHOTOGRAPHERS BLIND
28. WOODLAND POND
29. EROSION CONTROL DEVICES
30. WILDLIFE FOOD PATCHES
31. DISPLAY- SOILS & GEOLOGY OF AREA
32. GEOLOGY WALL
33. SOIL PIT
34. SLICE OF TIME STUDY
35. OBSERVATION TOWER
36. ROCK PILE
37. WILDFLOWER SANCTUARY
38. VEGETABLE GARDEN
39. HORTICULTURAL GARDENS
40. FOREST NURSERY

An outdoor laboratory is conducted at Ann Arbor, Michigan

Children learn gardening at a nature center in North Carolina

Visitors to W. K. Kellogg Sanctuary, Augusta, Michigan, become acquainted with Canada geese

needs to be planned carefully. An adequate parking area, preferably gravelled and black-topped is essential. The parking lot should be spacious and well laid out with a practical traffic pattern, including large enough entrances and exits. One section of it should be reserved for bicycles and a bike stall erected for this purpose.

Cost of a Nature Center

A community nature center costs money. The funds that are required are of two kinds: capital outlay expenditures (which include the initial investment in land, buildings and equipment) and annual operating funds.

To encourage and assist American communities in setting aside green islands of nature as centers for outdoor learning—focal points for nature appreciation, natural science study, and conservation education—the National Audubon Society has organized a Nature Centers Division that provides professional advice and guidance to individuals, organizations, schools, industrial firms, or government agencies in planning and developing conservation education centers on lands they already own or control.

Information about these services can be obtained by contacting the Nature Centers Division, National Audubon Society, 1130 Fifth Avenue, New York 10028. —J.J.S.

NATURE CRAFT PROJECTS
Things to Do With Nature Materials

It is an established fact that human beings, young and old, are interested in *doing* things with nature as well as *looking* at things. And for people who are just beginning to open their eyes to the many interesting things in nature, the *doing* has a great attraction.

In some school systems there is no time set aside for nature study. In others there is a small amount, a few minutes a week! In still others a goodly time is allowed. However, it is doubtful that there is any school system that would not be glad to have a teacher tuck in a few minutes each day, or week, when she could do a little nature study with the children in her room. It is a refreshing moment in the day for both teacher and children. It takes them outside of the schoolroom—in mind, anyway—and into a subject that no one will deny is broadening, often breathtaking, and that will be a help and a pleasure to children no matter where they go or what they do.

Here are some easy-to-do activities to try at school, club meetings, outdoors, or at home, after you have taken a short exploration trip around the block or through the yard to collect a few leaves and plants. If carefully carried out, attractive additions to nature notebooks, fine posters, and interesting exhibits for the school science room will result.

How to Make Prints of Leaves and Plants

Outline prints showing only the shapes of leaves and plants: Spatter prints make attractive posters, notebook covers, stationery, place cards. Use leaves, ferns, or even entire plants. Leaves whose margins are very much cut up or divided such as those of oak, locust, or ash, make more attractive spatter prints than those broadly oval such as elm, cherry, and apple. First flatten the flowers and leaves by pressing them for a half hour or so under a heavy book.

Materials needed:

Toothbrushes with stiff, even bristles.

Scrapers (knifeblades, nail files, or thin strips of wood).

Watercolors with containers for mixing and diluting to desired shade.

Paper that will absorb color readily (drawing paper).

Common pins.

Cigar box and fine window screen.

To make a print, fasten a leaf (smooth or topside down) to the paper with pins, heads of the pins toward the center. Pin all edges of leaf down firmly to make close contact with the paper. This insures definite outline of leaf. Dip brush into watercolor; shake out surplus water; hold (with bristles up) about two inches above paper and tilted toward paper at an angle of 45°. Scrape bristles lengthwise with knife and remember to scrape *towards you* or *you* will be spattered instead of the paper. Continue this scraping process evenly and firmly until the background is a satisfactory shade. Allow paper to dry, remove pins and leaf and print is complete.

To avoid danger of large drops of

Spatter print

Blue print

watercolor falling on paper, remove bottom and cover of cigar box and cover bottom with fine window screening. Place this frame over plant after it is pinned to paper and scrub screen gently with toothbrush dipped in watercolor. Only fine drops will fall to paper.

Many art supply stores carry colors for use on fabrics. With these it is possible to spatter print on cloth. These colors are fast and will wash.

Blueprints are a simple and easy type of nature outline prints. Materials needed:

Blueprint paper cut into pieces 8½ inches by 11 inches or 4¼ inches by 5½ inches. Purchase from blueprinting firm or architects' supply store and if possible have it cut into sheets of the desired size when ordering. Keep in a heavy wrapper in a dark dry place and for best results use soon after purchase.

Materials needed: Sheet of glass, about an inch larger all around than the sheets of blueprint paper. (Plate glass is much less breakable than ordinary glass.)

Two thicknesses of cotton flannel cloth, cut the size of the glass to form a pad.

Board or book, preferably the same size as glass.

Shallow pan of cold water (a little larger than sheets of blueprint paper).

Sunny day.

Arrange your specimen on the glass in subdued light, place blueprint paper (tinted side down) over specimen, and cover with pad and board or book. Pick up the whole thing (holding glass firmly in place with fingers) and carry into sunlight being careful not to cast a shadow across the glass or let fingers extend over paper. Expose to the light until paper turns blue and then fades to greenish-gray. Carry it into shade, remove paper and place (exposed side down) in a pan of cold water. Push paper down into the water to make sure it is thoroughly wet and leave in water for at least five minutes. (The paper can stay in water much longer without harm.) Remove paper and dry.

Ozalid prints are the reverse of blueprints in color and even easier to make. Materials needed:

Ozalid paper, often called dry print paper. Purchase from blueprinting firm or architects' supply store and if possible have it cut into sheets of the desired size when ordering. Ozalid paper comes in two colors, a dark, bright blue and a dull, brown-red.

Ozalid print

Sheets of glass, about an inch larger all around than the sheets of ozalid paper. (Plate glass is much less breakable than ordinary glass.)

Two thicknesses of cotton flannel cloth, cut the size of the glass, to form a pad.

Board or book, preferably the same size as glass.

Two-quart mason jar. Jar lid small enough to fit inside opening. Cotton or piece of cheesecloth to fit inside lid as absorbent pad. Concentrated ammonia (24–26 percent) usually obtainable from blueprint company or drugstore.

Arrange your specimen on the glass in subdued light, place ozalid paper (tinted side down) over specimen, and cover with board or book. Pick up the whole thing (holding glass firmly in place with fingers) and carry into sunlight being careful not to cast a shadow across the glass or let fingers extend over paper. Expose to direct sunlight until ozalid paper fades to pure white—about a minute. If young translucent leaves are used and an exposure of 10 to 15 minutes is allowed, the veins will show. Carry into shade, remove paper, roll into cylinder, and thrust up into printing jar. (Set up printing jar by inverting mason jar over lid containing cotton or cheesecloth pad to which a small quantity of ammonia has been added.) Print will appear as if by magic. Print until dark blue or red. If print is mottled, the exposure to sunlight was not long enough. Prints can be made with household ammonia, but a longer time is required. CAUTION— Whether concentrated or household ammonia is used, the fumes are strong. Care should be taken to avoid inhaling fumes.

When buying either blueprint or ozalid paper, mention that you intend printing by sunlight. These papers come in different speeds. A medium speed is usually more desirable.

Detail prints showing veins and margins of leaves and plants. Crayon prints are easily made, even by small children,

and require nothing more complicated than some crayons, notebook paper, and perhaps scissors and paste.

Lay a leaf, vein side up, on something with a firm, smooth surface. Place a sheet of notebook paper over the leaf. Hold this securely in place and rub the *side* of a soft crayon, from which all paper has been removed, over the paper, making all the strokes go the same way. Almost like magic, the form and veins of the leaf will appear on the paper. Almost everyone has done this kind of printing when a child—usually by placing a penny under the paper, or a nickel if one was so fortunate as to have one. To make a neater appearing print, cut out the leaf print carefully and mount on cardboard or another sheet of paper. A soft black lead pencil with broad flat point or colored pencils may be substituted for the crayon, if desired.

Ink-pad prints are easy to make on a nature hike because the equipment is so simple and light to carry. Materials:

Notebook paper.

Ink pad (such as is used for rubber stamps and obtainable in various colors and sizes).

Newspaper cut to fit the ink pad.

Place a leaf on the ink pad, vein side down, cover with newspaper and rub to

Ink print

ink it. Place leaf inked side down on note paper, cover with a clean piece of newspaper and rub gently but firmly, being careful not to let the leaf slip on the paper, or its impression will be blurred. Be sure that the print is thoroughly dry before touching.

Smoke prints are often considered the most attractive of nature prints but special care is needed in making them to avoid any possibility of accident.

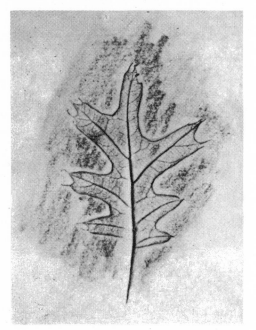

Smoke print

Since any accident usually indicates carelessness, forewarned should mean forearmed. The essential materials are:

Grease (lard or some commercial substitute).

Newspapers.

Candles (slow-burning plumber's candles are best).

Notebook paper (smooth unglazed surface).

One-fourth of a file folder is large enough for one print. Apply a little dab of grease to the folder. Rub it into the paper thoroughly. Use only a small quantity of grease since it takes very little to cover a space large enough for a leaf. Hold the paper to the light and look for lines of unabsorbed grease. If there are any, rub them into the paper, otherwise they will spoil the print. When a space large enough for the leaf has been covered by the grease hold the *greased portion* of the paper, greased side down, overhead and move candle flame back and forth rapidly under *greased portion.*

CAUTION—Do not let ungreased parts of the paper get into flame as these will scorch and may burn.

When the greased part of the folder is well covered with a layer of carbon (looks jet black), place it, blackened side up, on the table. Lay the leaf, underside down, on the center of the carboned paper and cover with a piece of newspaper. With the fingers of the left hand hold the tip and the "stem" of the leaf firmly in place under the top sheet of paper. With the finger cushions of the right hand, rub diligently the area of the sheet covering the leaf, being sure that neither the leaf nor the papers move.

When every vein and outline of the leaf are visible through the piece of newspaper, remove the paper and pick up the leaf. Place the leaf, carboned side down, on a piece of notepaper and cover it with a clean piece of newspaper and rub as before. Again make certain that neither the leaf nor the papers move. When the veins and outline again stand out, your print is completed. If properly done a leaf print made by this method looks like an etching. Every tiny vein shows. The print is permanent and will not rub.

How to Make Plaster Casts of Footprints, Leaves, Nuts

Along beaches, muddy borders of streams, muddy banks in the city park or even in a wet corner of your school yard, the tracks or footprints of a variety of birds and other animals are often found. By means of plaster of paris these tracks can be permanently recorded and make an interesting exhibit for your school science room. Materials needed:

Plaster of paris (inexpensive at hardware, drug, and artist supply stores).

Water, talcum powder, grease.

Small can or cup for mixing.

Narrow strips of cardboard.

Paper clips.

Animal tracks sharply outlined and sunken about one-half inch in mud make the best casts. Find a good footprint and sprinkle lightly with talcum powder. Using the cardboard strips, make a low fence around it, joining the ends with paper clips; the enclosure may be round, square, or whatever shape desired. The fence is not essential but it does make a neater cast. Mix plaster with water (of sufficient amount to fill track to top of fence) to about the density of pancake batter, stirring briskly to make it smooth. Pour gently into the track. When the cast is hard (15 to 20 minutes later) lift it carefully and allow to dry thoroughly before scrubbing off the mud and dirt (*See under Animal: Animal Tracks*).

It is fun to use these negative casts to make footprints in a box of wet sand or mud. These casts can also be used to make permanent footprints in wet cement. A short cement walk on your nature trail or leading to your nature museum can be made very interesting if stamped, when wet, with footprints of wild animals of the area. Collect casts and try it.

A positive cast is made by covering the surface of the negative cast with grease (any kind—lard, vaseline, other), placing a cardboard collar around it, and pouring plaster of paris into it.

How to Make Insect "Apartments"

Insect cages are good things to have on your window sill, nature shelf, or in your science room, and here are directions for making one. Take the lids of two tin cans (baking powder, cocoa, or use the little metal boxes typewriter

Crayon print

ribbons come in), a piece of copper or galvanized window screening, some plaster of paris, and a twig. In one can top put the screening, bent to fit, and with overlapping edges tied with fine wire or with string, so there will be no openings through which your guests might inadvertently escape. Into the bottom of this can top pour a little plaster of paris to hold the screen in place and form a floor, and just as it begins to harden insert the twig and hold it in place for a few minutes until the plaster has fully hardened. This twig is to give the insects something to climb on. Use the other can top for a removable cover. Put a little soil or grass in the bottom to make it homelike.

Paper ice cream containers also make good insect apartments. Cut a window on each side. Cover one with cheesecloth or screen held in place with tape. Cover the other with cellophane so you can see inside.

Conservation Is an Important "Thing to Do in Nature"

No matter how little or how much we do with nature in our schools, our homes, our communities, and national organizations, the one thing we cannot afford to lose sight of is the opportunity to help ourselves and others to see the value of conservation in relation to our own human lives. Teaching this concept follows very naturally and easily any sort of nature activity which brings about discussion and interest.

To conserve means to keep in a safe or sound state. And if we really mean it when we say we are conservationists, we should be willing and anxious to keep *all forms* of life in a safe and sound condition. This means removing from our minds that any *one* form of wildlife is more worthy to be saved than any other. It means acceptance of the fact that all forms of life—the snake, the bird, the toad, the earthworm, the bat, the deer, and so on, have their rightful place in the scheme of nature. Destroy the natural enemy of any form of life and it soon turns out that man has destroyed the thing he has tried to save (*See under Balance of Nature: Biological Control; and under Predators*).

One must try to understand and remember that when man destroys one form of wildlife this is depriving another form of wildlife of its food. For instance, kill all the insects and what are insect-eating birds to do?

Some people are very apt to have prejudices against certain forms of animal life—snakes, for example. Once a black snake was clubbed to death because it had "dared" to go up a tree and help itself to a young robin. The person who did the clubbing sat down to a dinner of good lamb chops and did not seem to see the irony of the situation. Man raises sheep that other men may have lamb chops. Nature raises extra birds that the black snakes may eat and live. There is nothing cruel about this. One thing *preys* upon another—one thing *feeds* upon another. It all depends upon how one wants to look at it.

It is only through close and constant association with the things out of doors that one finally understands that he must gain an insight into the balance of nature before he can do a constructive job of conservation.

The wildlife of the country is in the keeping and at the mercy of each succeeding generation of human beings. Therefore, it behooves each person to give some careful thought to what he does in his treatment of the wild animals and plants of the American out-of-doors. (*See also under Aquarium; Insect: Insects in the classroom; Plant: Indoor Plants; Nature Quiz*)   —M.E.G

Recommended Reading

The Amateur Naturalist's Handbook—Vinson Brown. Little, Brown & Company, Boston.
The Book of Nature Hobbies—Ted Pettit. Didier Publishing Company, New York.
Field Book of Nature Activities—William Hillcourt. G. P. Putnam's Sons, New York.
Golden Book of Nature Crafts: Hobbies and Activities for Boys and Girls—John R. Saunders. Simon & Schuster, New York.
Leader's Nature Guide: How to do Nature Before She Does You—Marie E. Gaudette. Girl Scouts of the U. S. A., New York.
Projects and Activities—National Audubon Society, New York.
The Wonders I See—John K. Terres. J. B. Lippincott Company, Philadelphia.

NATURE EXPLORATION
Adventures in Viewpoint

On the thirtieth day of January 1841, Henry Thoreau set down in his journal this record of a small adventure in the snow-covered fields of Concord.

"Looking down the river," he wrote, "I saw a fox some sixty rods off making across the fields to my left. As the snow lay five inches deep, he made but slow progress; but it was no impediment to me. So, yielding to the instinct of the chase, I tossed my head aloft and bounded away, snuffing the air like a foxhound, and spurning the world and human society at each bound. It seemed the woods rang with the hunter's horn and Diana and all the satyrs joined in the chase and cheered me on."

Thus, for a few exhilarating moments, Henry Thoreau entered another world than his own. They are all about—these other worlds—the world of the fox, the squirrel, the beetle, the fish, the bird. One needs only the keys of curiosity and imagination to enter their infinite variety. Adventures in viewpoint are within the reach of all.

When, like Thoreau, one imagines himself part of another realm—whether it is the weedy, water-world of the perch, the grass jungles of the katydid, the mossy well of the frog, the hot, conical sand pit of the ant-lion, the white foam-castle of the tiny froghopper, the fungus forests of the beetle, or the dark haunts of the earthworm and the mole—one is exploring as surely as if he were journeying across a tundra or through the rain forest of some remote land.

To stop and wonder, to put oneself for a passing moment in the place of the creatures around him—to visualize life from their standpoint—here, truly, is an adventure in exploring. Such journeys require neither rubber tires nor gasoline. They take only leisure moments from one's time. And they are just as possible for a man on a park bench, or a woman in an apartment window, as they are for a wanderer in the open fields. . . .

On city streets one's eyes may follow dusty sparrows flying, with trailing straws, to half-built nests on ledges high above the traffic. One may walk on, oblivious to other events around him, but the mind may be busy visualizing life on that high ledge, life in storm and wind and rain and blistering heat, an existence in which the life preservers of wings play so large a part. Again, one may look out of an upper window into the treetop world of a maple or spruce where a squirrel scurries in fits and starts along a limb or where a spider spread its aerial net among the bluish needles of the evergreen. And in moments that follow, one's surroundings may fall away and he gives himself to

the delights of picturing in vivid detail how life must appear from the viewpoint of an arboreal existence.

These adventures of the mind are all about, in city or country. One summer day look across a freshwater marsh below an orchard hillside, and see red-winged blackbirds drop into the waving masses of windblown cattails as though they were diving into the breakers of a green sea. Here and there the sunlight glints on the wings of dragonflies. Wonder then, how the marsh forest, the wide cattail islands with their thousands of waving sword leaves, must appear to the dragonfly, the blackbird, and the ant, living among the dense vegetation of this marshland jungle. Find out by slipping into rubber boots, and, with the *Oka-leeee!* of the blackbirds ringing in one's ears, wade across a hundred yards of sloshy marsh grass made treacherous by the tunneling of muskrats. From where one stands, the masses of whitish blooms of the climbing boneset are sharp against the dense stand of cattails like splotches of foam on waves of dark green water. . . .

There, among the cattails, stop and tramp down a little cave amid them, sit down, and look about. Here one has the viewpoint of the blackbird in its swaying basket nest, of the dragonfly clinging to its upright stalk, of the ant running along the natural suspension bridge of a boneset creeper. On all sides arise the slender columns of the cattails, old and new, brown and green. Sunlight, slanting downward, is diffused into the soft illumination of the marsh bottom. Over the black and glistening mud run ghostly white creepers, and decaying cattail leaves lie crisscrossed like the cane seat of a discolored chair. . . .

When a quick gust strikes the cattail island, a multitude of bladelike leaves wave against the sky above one's head. The stiff brown cattails nod gravely among the wild flutter of their leaves. The wind passes and the flutter ebbs away. In the hot, moist silence that follows, bits of fluff drift down from the

The honeybee uses its long tongue to dine on nectc

older stalks, dropping slowly and silently as though descending through water.

Tens of thousands of these floating seeds can come from a single cattail. One winter day carry home an average-sized cattail seed-head and begin counting the seeds at the ends of their parachutes of fluff. Divide the cattail into half-inch sections, and set to work.

At the end of a whole evening's labor, one can account for hardly more than those seeds a red-winged blackbird can pull out with one thrust of its beak. Night after night, the count can go grimly on. Thousands, tens of thousands, of seeds can be recorded in this one-person cattail-seed census, and more than ten days later it may be revealed that the single head contained 147,265 closepacked seeds.

From outside one's little cave in the marsh tangle come other sounds, each bringing to one its mental picture. The creaking clatter of the marsh wren, for all the world like the noise of a miniature, unoiled lawnmower, arouses in the mind's eye a vision of its little body on vibrating wings rising a dozen feet into the air and then dropping back into the cattails again in the manner of those tiny helicopters one sent aloft as a boy. There are other noises—the far-carrying yelp of a dog, the faint drone of a high-flying plane, the cry of a gull coasting across a little patch of sky above one's cavern in the cattail marsh.

The air around is filled with the faint sweetish perfume of the boneset blooms. In a cluster, hardly more than an inch in diameter, there are 40 flowerets. Close beside, a wild bee alights. Grasping a small clump of blooms with its forelegs, as though holding a goblet, it runs its long tongue into floweret after floweret. Brilliant little gold-banded flies walk up and down the green highways of the cattail leaves. Basking in the sun on one dying leaf . . . is a fly with pinkish eyes, gold-white stripes down its face, and a tail tipped with red. Below, on the floor of the cavern where an old cattail lies like a burst bomb, a gray fly with reddish eyes washes its face, kittenwise, over and over again.

Single-file, three black ants hurry across a boneset bridge and disappear into a tangle of cattails beyond. A yellowish mass, dimly seen through the leaves, attracts one's eyes. A quick investigation reveals it is the abandoned nest of a long-billed marsh wren—a six-inch oval of twisted cattail leaves lined with fluff. The doorway is almost entirely closed. Poke an investigating finger inside. Instantly, a stream of dark little ants pours from the interior. The nest is the penthouse home of an ant colony.

In their excitement some of the insects, carrying white pupae in their jaws, drop fully three feet downward to the wet, glistening plants below. Five minutes later, when their fright has passed away, one sees these same ants, unhurt by their fall, toiling up the cattails again with their precious pupae still clutched in their jaws. . . . Hunting and travel for the ants was made possible only by the endless crisscrossing and interlacing of narrow leaves. Their whole lives may be spent in an unstable world of moving leaves. . . .

For a long time stand watching the hurried labors of these semi-aerial insects. Successive gusts sweep across the island, their progress recorded by the cattails first bending all one way, then holding the position for a moment, and finally rising erect once more. When the upper leaves move in the wind, their shadows run swiftly up and down the stalks of their neighbors. The sun swings lower in the west.

Stoop and push one's way out of the opening he has made in the cattail world. Beyond, he may see the familiar trees and gardens of an upland hillside. Straighten up once more and it is like closing a door behind one. But, never again will that cattail island seem the same. Henceforth, it will always be associated with an adventure in near-at-home exploring. One has seen it from a fresh viewpoint, and for part of a summer afternoon, he has lived within the depths of another world.   —E.W.T.

Recommended Reading

Adventures in Nature—Edwin Way Teale. Dodd, Mead & Company, New York.
Grassroot Jungles—Edwin Way Teale. Dodd, Mead & Company, New York.

NATURE HOBBIES

Outdoor hobbies for people interested in nature are almost as numerous as the nature subjects themselves. People collect shells (*see under Mollusk and under Snail*); insects (*see under Insect: Insects in the Classroom and under Insects of Ponds and Streams*); rocks (*see under Rock Formation*); plants, and a host of other natural history objects. From collecting as a hobby, people learn to know animals and plants as they can get to know them in few other ways (birds and mammals are an exception as they can be studied in nature through binoculars). Many fishes, toads, frogs, salamanders, snakes, and lizards can be kept and their habits studied in the home aquarium (*see Aquarium*) or in the terrarium (*See Terrarium*).

Nature photography has become one of the most popular of all outdoor nature hobbies. From fine photographs and the techniques of obtaining them, nature photographers have contributed to our knowledge of wild birds and other animals, and have themselves learned much about their subjects (*See Nature Photography*). Birdwatching or studying and identifying birds as an outdoor nature hobby is one of the most popular of all as evidenced by the material in many volumes of The Audubon Nature Encyclopedia.

As a part of the birdwatching hobby, attracting birds to one's yard or garden has become one of the most popular of all. One does not need to know the birds, or to be able to identify them, to attract them. Learning to identify birds can

A dragonfly rests on a cattail leaf

come later, after the birds are coming to the feeders in one's yard or garden, or nesting in the birdhouses one can put up to attract some of them. Planting trees and shrubs to attract birds is also a part of any bird-attracting program (*See Plants and Water for Birds*).

On the following pages are some simple and effective methods of attracting birds that may be followed by anyone. They will offer an introduction to an engrossing and satisfying hobby that may last throughout one's lifetime.   —J.K.T.

Recommended Reading

The Book of Bird Life—A. A. Allen. D. Van Nostrand Company, Inc. Princeton, New Jersey.
Homes for Birds—W. L. McAtee, Conservation Bulletin No. 14, United States Government Printing Office, Washington, D.C.
Songbirds in Your Garden—John K. Terres. Thomas Y. Crowell Company, New York.

Gourd Bird House

Nesting Material Holder

Bluebird House

Nuthatch House

Wren House

Glass Backed Weather-proof Bird Feeder

Suet Holder

Window Shelf Bird Feeder

Old Christmas T

Martin House

Robin Nest Shelf

Sparrow Hawk or Kestrel House

Rustic Screech Owl House

Phoebe Nest Shelf

Nest Box

Window Shelf Bird Feeder

fe Feeding Shelter

Suet Holder

Coconut Shell Bird Feeder

Tin Can Bird Feeder

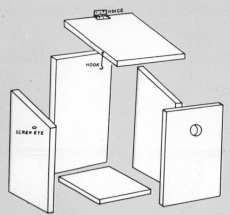

Basic plan for simple birdhouse. Vary dimensions to suit species desired.

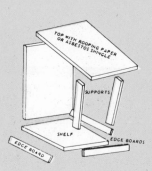

Nesting shelf for robins

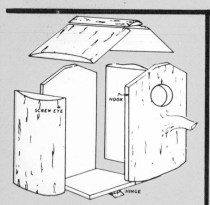

Rustic birdhouse made from slabs

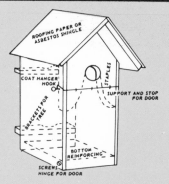

"Dave Cook Special" birdhouse made from orange crate

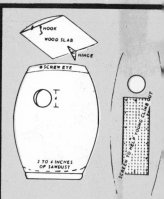

Nail keg wood duck house

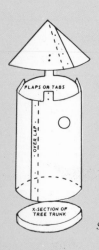

Roof of tar paper birdhouse

Tar paper birdhouse

Simple wren house

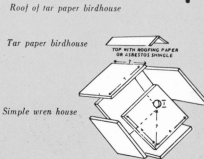

Martin house

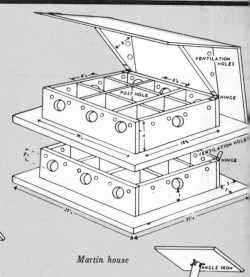

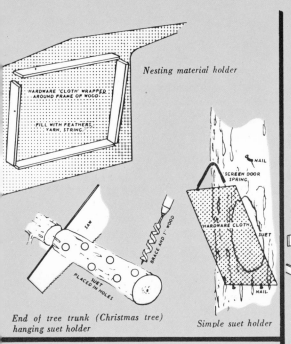

Nesting material holder

HARDWARE 'CLOTH' WRAPPED AROUND FRAME OF WOOD.

FILL WITH FEATHERS, YARN, STRING.

SAW

BRACE AND 1" WOOD

SUET PLACED IN HOLES

End of tree trunk (Christmas tree) hanging suet holder

NAIL

SCREEN DOOR SPRING

HARDWARE CLOTH

SUET

NAIL

Simple suet holder

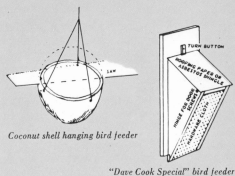

SAW

Coconut shell hanging bird feeder

TURN BUTTON

ROOFING PAPER OR ASBESTOS SHINGLE

HINGE FOR DOOR SCREEN

HARDWARE CLOTH

"Dave Cook Special" bird feeder

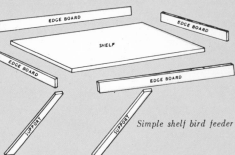

EDGE BOARD

EDGE BOARD

SHELF

EDGE BOARD

EDGE BOARD

SUPPORT

SUPPORT

Simple shelf bird feeder

HINGE

HARDWARE CLOTH

DOOR

BIRDS ENTER HERE

HARDWARE CLOTH

FOOD TRAY

HOOK

"Dennis Shaw" bird feeder

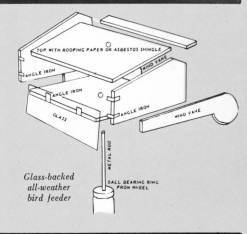

TOP WITH ROOFING PAPER OR ASBESTOS SHINGLE

ANGLE IRON

WIND VANE

ANGLE IRON

ANGLE IRON

GLASS

WIND VANE

METAL ROD

BALL BEARING RING FROM WHEEL

Glass-backed all-weather bird feeder

SPECIES OF BIRD	DIMENSIONS OF HOUSE				
	Floor Space	Height	Hole above Floor	Diameter of Hole	Distance above Ground
House Wren	4 in. x 4 in.	6 in. to 10 in.	6 in. to 9 in.	1 in.	8 ft. to 20 ft.
Chickadee, Nuthatch, Downy Woodpecker	4 in. x 4 in.	7 in. to 11 in.	6 in. to 10 in.	1¼ in.	5 ft. to 25 ft.
Tree Swallow	5 in. x 5 in.	6 in. to 10 in.	5 in. to 8 in.	1½ in.	5 ft. to 25 ft.
Eastern Bluebird	5 in. x 5 in.	8 in. to 12 in.	6 in. to 10 in.	1½ in.	5 ft. to 20 ft.
Crested Flycatcher	6 in. x 6 in.	8 in. to 14 in.	6 in. to 12 in.	2 in.	10 ft. to 40 ft.
Flicker	7 in. x 7 in.	8 in. to 18 in.	6 in. to 16 in.	2½ in.	10 ft. to 25 ft.
Woodduck, Hooded Merganser	8 in. x 8 in.	14 in. to 20 in.	12 in. to 15 in.	4 in.	10 ft. to 25 ft.
Sparrow Hawk or Kestrel, Saw-Whet Owl	7 in. x 7 in.	16 in. to 18 in.	13 in. to 17 in.	3 in.	20 ft. to 50 ft.
Screech Owl	8 in. x 10 in.	12 in. to 18 in.	10 in. to 17 in.	3¼ in.	10 ft. to 30 ft.
English or House Sparrow (Nest Box)	5 in. x 6 in.			Open	10 ft. to 30 ft.
Robin (Nest Shelf)	6 in. x 8 in.				10 ft. to 30 ft.
Phoebe (Nest Shelf)	4 in. x 7 in.				5 ft. to 25 ft.

1. Nesting shelves for robins may be placed on trees or the sides of buildings; nesting shelves for phoebes should be placed under eaves, bridges, or in old barns or buildings.

2. Martin houses should be placed 10 to 20 feet from the ground in the open. For more secure fastening, the post is extended through the center of the house to the roof.

3. Tar paper bird houses are cheap to make but are temporary structures, seldom lasting more than two seasons. The top is made from a circle of tar paper from which a wedge has been removed. Soft aluminum rivets are used for assembly. The bottom is attached last and is held in position with copper tacks. A small gap should be left between roof and sides for ventilation.

4. Owl houses are most effective if placed in an inconspicuous location.

Care and Feeding of Orphaned Birds

Every year birds' nests are blown out of trees by violent storms and newly hatched or half-grown young birds scattered on the ground. If the nest and fledglings can be replaced in the tree or bush, it is far better to do so and let the bird-parents go on with an exacting job for which they alone are best suited. But if you enjoy being a foster parent, the experience of establishing a nursery for young birds can be rewarding. When the nest has been destroyed, and the youngsters seem doomed to perish without your care, take them in if you are prepared to devote yourself to the task of feeding them at 15-minute intervals for at least 12 hours during the day.

If the nest has been destroyed, put the helpless young birds in a box in a substitute nest, perhaps of grass, lined with soft cloth or cotton so that the birds' feet have something pliable to push against. Keep them warm by covering them with a cloth and protecting them from drafts. If the fledglings are old enough to perch, put them in a large cage, or better, give them the freedom of a room in which they can learn to fly.

Young birds should be handled as little as possible and not fed too much at a time. Feed them only during daylight hours, but feedings should be frequent, at least every 15 minutes, or, at most, half an hour apart. Young birds are like children; they demand all the attention they can get, but regularity of feeding gives the best results.

Foods and Feeding

Feeding is common sense, with a dash of ingenuity. Many people try to feed foundling wild birds simply on bread, even offering it to owls and grebes.

A basic food for very young songbird nestlings, other than hummingbirds, is equal parts of finely mashed yolk of hard-boiled eggs and finely sifted bread crumbs, *slightly* moistened with milk or cod-liver oil. This mixture will agree with starlings, blue jays, cardinals, tow-hees, robins, catbirds, orioles, sparrows and other small birds. Good supplementary foods are canned dog food, bits of grapes, cherries, bananas, or soft apple pulp, pieces of earthworms that have been "squeezed out," and bits of scraped or finely chopped meat. One woman with an orphaned yellow-billed cuckoo got a supply of insects for it each night by attracting insects to a light in her window.

At first, older fledglings may not eat. To force-feed them, hold the bird by enclosing its body and closed wings in your left hand, and with your forefinger and thumb, gently pry open the bill at its base. In your right hand hold a medicine dropper, or an improvised narrow wooden spoon, or better, with your fingers pick up a small moist ball of food. Poke the food down the bird's throat, but not too much at once or it will choke. In a short time the youngsters will learn to open their bills for the food. Continue the feeding until the bird's crop is full, and it should be especially full at nightfall, just before the bird goes to sleep.

To supplement the basic diet, include chopped nasturtium and watercress, rich in calcium and vitamins, and cottage cheese for added protein.

Most seed-eaters—cardinals, grosbeaks, and finches—also need fine gravel and charcoal, crushed seeds, chopped greens, fruits, mealworms and insects.

Young woodpeckers eat a mixture of dog food and the basic finely mashed egg yolks.

For baby hummingbirds supply a syrup in one part of sugar to two or three parts of water fed with a medicine dropper. After about 10 days, feed the hummers their first protein—dried dog food very finely sifted and thoroughly mixed with the syrup.

Young hawks and owls require meat, preferably meat with the fur or feathers on it which aids the digestion of raptorial birds. Feed them on freshly caught rats and mice, or poultry and raw beef sprinkled with cod-liver oil, with which chicken feathers may be mixed.

Water and Sunshine

Small birds are quickly killed by forcibly giving them water. Before they learn to drink, they receive sufficient water for their needs from their food. When they are old enough to sit on a perch, water may be offered in a shallow dish. You may then dip their bills into a water cup until they learn to drink by themselves. Young birds must have some sunshine too, but they should be shaded from the heat of the midday sun. Birds, like humans, welcome a cool retreat in hot weather.

When hand feeding a bird, it should be held in a firm but gentle grasp allowing its feet to rest on one's little finger

When the Bird Grows up

No matter how attached one may become to the bird raised, he must remember that he has been a protector, not a captor, and that wild birds belong to the state. As soon as a bird is strong enough, it should be allowed to forage for itself and should be turned loose as soon as it is able to fly. If the foundlings are not encouraged to return to a wild, free life, they will learn to depend upon human assistance which may bring them disaster when they are suddenly thrown upon their own.

Nesting Material for Birds

Ordinarily, birds find enough materials with which to build their nests, but in some well-pruned and carefully raked yards, nesting materials may be scarce. Birds are strikingly adaptive creatures and often will weave into their nests manufactured goods resembling grasses, rootlets, spider webs, animal hairs, and other ordinarily available natural supplies.

Orioles will use yarns, strings, and floss; goldfinches will use cotton; cardinals will use colored threads. String-like material should be cut into 8- or 10-inch lengths, for if the strings are too long, the birds may get entangled in them disastrously. White or dull-colored strings or yarn are safest to offer birds because bright-colored material, woven in the nest, may attract attention to nests that should remain concealed.

One manufacturer makes a nesting material "supply house" of four compartments which may be nailed to a tree, post, or other convenient place in the yard. Each apartment contains hemp, wool, horsehair, or sphagnum moss, and birds may come here to choose what suits them best and help themselves. Later, this supply house may be used as a suet-holder when the nest-building season is over. —J.K.T.

Recommended Reading

Baby Sitter for Chimney Swifts — Margaret Whittemore. *Audubon Magazine,* May-June 1948.
Experience With Fledglings — Sara Menaboni, *Audubon Magazine,* May-June 1944.
Food! Food! Food! — Josephine V. Wilis. *Audubon Magazine,* Jan-Feb. 1947.
Homer the 6th Grade Grackle — Elizabeth B. Clarkson. *Audubon Magazine,* Sept.-Oct. 1948.
An Owl Friend of Mine — James B. Young. *Audubon Magazine,* Sept.-Oct., 1945.
The Owl Who Went to College — Virginia Orr. *Audubon Magazine,* Sept.- Oct. 1947.
Personalities in Feathers — Gertrude V. Grover. *Audubon Magazine,* Jan.-Feb. 1945.
A Thrasher Talks His Way to Fame — Marie V. Beal. *Audubon Magazine,* Sept.-Oct. 1942.
Tribulations of a Sparrow Rancher — George M. Sutton. *Audubon Magazine,* Sept.-Oct. 1948.

NATURE PHOTOGRAPHY

For an increasing number of teachers, youth leaders, and hobbyists, interest in nature is finding expression in photography. Their trips into forests, mountains, and deserts, or along rivers and coasts are providing them with many chances to bring back colorful slides and other useful and interesting pictures.

Gunsight cameras permit the photographer to follow moving subjects easily

Camera fans, too, are discovering in nature a challenging new field of photography.

No matter where one lives, there is bound to be something worth photographing in the natural world surrounding one. One person may spend years photographing the endless variety of insects in his backyard and nearby apple orchard. Another may attract birds to his garden the year round by providing food and nesting boxes within range of his lenses. Few nature photographers can pass a wild flower without attempting to photograph it. An increasing number are now recording in pictures the amazing life of the plant world—mosses, lichens, slime molds, and small fungi. With the small, lightweight cameras, fast color film, excellent lenses of various focal lengths, and compact strobelight units now available, nearly every naturalist considers photography an invaluable asset to his hobby or profession. He can capture variations in color and size of an animal, and with rapid sequence cameras he can get many still pictures of a bird in flight, feeding, or nest-building.

Through the ages many men have found satisfaction and pleasure in hunting or collecting. But as many forms of wildlife became more scarce, more and more outdoorsmen have turned to the camera as a way of recording the thrill of the chase through photography, having their game and leaving it for others to see another day.

Most photographers specialize, concentrating on particular types of pictures or subjects—artistic compositions of color and form; sharp, graphic pictures for illustrations and identification; pictures that show characteristics and behavior of the subjects. Some photographers have the eyes of an artist; others have the eyes of a scientist. Some, with an ecologist's view, will show their photographic subject in relation to its environment.

To the naturalist, a photographic series has special appeal since it offers a chance to combine a number of approaches, and to tell a story—as, for example, the life of a stream, or a day in the forest.

Equipment

The type of camera, lens, film, and accessories one needs will vary with the subjects one attempts to photograph. The amount of time one can devote to nature photography will have an important bearing on what equipment to get. So, of course, will its cost.

The most popular cameras for nature photography are single-lens and twin-lens reflex cameras. These come in different film sizes, from the 5 by 7 inches down to the 35 millimeter. Their great advantage is that focusing and composition is done through the lens that takes the picture (in the single-lens reflex), or through a viewing lens directly connected to the lens that takes the picture (the twin-lens reflex).

Most single-lens reflex cameras have interchangeable lenses, while twin-lens reflex cameras generally do not have the interchangeable lens or extension bellows feature. For closeup work there are attachments—"portrait lenses"—which enable one to get larger film images. When one wants to photograph subjects that are wary and cannot be closely approached, he can attach a longer focal length lens and so get a larger image on the film. Some of these cameras, such as the Graflex, have bellows that extend, so that large images of small subjects can be made.

Cameras not focused through the lens utilize a range finder, either built in or separate. For subjects that are moving or require fast shooting, the focusing must be done quickly.

Films should be chosen to suit one's subject and purpose. This choice may also determine what camera to use. The greater the negative size the less it will need to be enlarged. But the larger the negative or color transparency the higher the cost per picture. If one's subjects are in motion, then a faster film is needed—because a faster shutter speed must be used and less light will reach the film. In this case, the film must be more sensitive to capture the subject in less time. If one wants color transparencies for projecting on a screen, he may use either the 35 millimeter or 2¼ by 2¼ inch size.

Whatever combination of camera and film is used, the next important item for use is a tripod. Most experienced photographers use them when shooting close-ups or when using telephoto lenses. Also they use a cable release and watch the subject to catch the right moment to trip the shutter, without having to

Twin-lens reflex cameras photograph subjects as close as three feet. With attachments they can be focused to 11 inches

Single-lens reflex cameras with extension tubes and a telephoto lens make extreme enlargement from a distance possible

keep an eye at the finder. A tripod also will allow the focus to be held on very close objects. It also will allow slower shutter speeds when more depth of field is needed and long focal length lenses can be used without fear of the magnified image being blurred by slight movement. Of course, for fast action or flight shots, a tripod may not be practical.

For wary subjects that frequent water holes and feeding areas or that occupy special perches, a *blind* may be necessary, or the camera may be operated by remote control. The blind is a structure that conceals the cameraman from the birds or other animals he wishes to photograph. It may be constructed with burlap stretched over a framework large enough to accommodate the photographer with his camera.

The versatile 4-by-5-inch press camera has extension bellows, ground glass focusing, many shutter speeds, and a choice of lenses

With some experience one will know how close to put the blind to the nest, runway, or other spot that the subject visits. From inside the blind one will be able to focus, rewind film, and even change lenses without being seen. Even though hidden, the photographer should be sure to move *slowly* and avoid making any noise. Most animals are frightened off by unexpected sounds or movements.

If one does not have or want to use a blind, a remote control device will provide a way to get closeup pictures of birds or other wild animals. Some cameras, if securely anchored, can be operated from a distance by attaching a long string to the shutter. The camera is set up on a tripod, focused on a nest, perch, or runway, and the release string run from the camera to a spot where the photographer can watch from a more or less concealed position. When the subject is in the right place the string is pulled and the shutter released. If the photographer uses a solenoid on the camera, a battery or flashgun can be used to trip the shutter while he watches from a distance. Either flashbulbs or strobe light can be used with this remote control, as well as in other situations.

In deep woods or where the subject is partly in shadows, supplementary light is often needed to get clear pictures. This is especially true when using color film. In cloudy weather, early or late in the day and in woods or deep shadow, one may depend completely on flashbulbs or strobe light for extra lighting. But in sunlight, especially with color film, flash also may be needed to illuminate the shadows which otherwise would be dark and uninteresting. If one cannot use artificial light to fill in shadow areas, an aluminum foil reflector to shine light into shadowy places may serve the same purpose.

Upon examination of one's pictures, it will frequently be found that the subjects are lost against the details of their surroundings. To avoid this, a plain background may be placed behind the subject, far enough back to avoid shadows that the object might cast.

The foregoing discussion has pertained to the use of still cameras but for the most part the same holds for motion picture cameras. The principles of lens use and composition are essentially the same. In motion picture photography a tripod is even more important. Since a movie camera actually takes a great number of still pictures, one after the other, and at a relatively slow shutter speed, the camera must be very steady. This becomes more important as the focal length of the lens is increased. A magnified image will tolerate less movement in the camera. Lighting is a greater problem with the motion picture camera for the subject must have *constant* light. For all practical purposes the sun, aided by a reflector, is satisfactory.

Birds

More persons have been attracted to photographing birds than to any other group of animal subjects. Most birds usually are easier to approach with a camera than most mammals. Then too, they are more numerous and colorful. For bird photography, long focal length lenses, fast shutters, and quick focusing devices are preferred. Except when on the nest, most birds are flitting, hopping, or flying about.

If one can discover the perch where a particular bird will sit to preen or wait for passing insects he can set up a blind or remote control and wait till the bird returns and then wait for just the right pose and snap the picture. This is the way many bird pictures are taken. The camera is prefocused, the picture composed to suit the eye, and even the flash for supplementary lighting may be arranged.

Feeding stations and nesting boxes provide excellent opportunities for photographing birds. Birds become accustomed to people and a camera can be set quite near them without their becoming alarmed. Shutter speeds of at least 1/150th of a second are needed to stop most action. Slower speeds can sometimes be used if one waits until the bird settles down on its nest. As a bird comes in to feed its young it commonly will pause for a moment, giving a chance for a good "action" shot. Pictures of birds on the nest are relatively easy to take.   It should be remembered that both eggs and young are delicate and can stand, for only a short time, exposure to hot sun or chilling air. One should not persist if the parents stay away. *One's first regard must be for his wild animal subject.* Satisfaction comes from getting good pictures without endangering the bird or other creature photographed.

Flight shots of birds are more difficult to get. One must either focus quickly as he follows the bird or estimate the distance from camera to bird beforehand. A fast shutter speed and fast film emulsion should be used. The bird should be in focus but it is not always necessary to completely stop all motion. Sometimes a slight blur to the wing tips adds to the feeling of flight. It has been found, when photographing birds in a flock, that by setting the lens at a given distance and waiting for one of the birds to fly into range, one may be able to get better results than by trying to follow the flock with the camera.

For shorebirds, an effective method is for the photographer to focus the camera on a certain part of the beach along the water's edge and put a small rock or stick just outside of the picture area. Then he should have someone drive the birds slowly past the spot where the camera is focused. One will be able to arrange such setups by closely observing the habits of different species. Much of the fun is in "outwitting" these normally cautious and wary creatures.

Mammals

Mammals are difficult to photograph.

They are wary, none too obvious, and many are nocturnal. They are not impossible to photograph but do require some skill, ingenuity, and a considerable knowledge of the habits of each species. Many animals that live in dens or burrows, such as the woodchuck, badger, skunk, and sometimes foxes and coyotes, can be photographed by a remote control device.

Young foxes and coyotes play around the openings of their dens even in bright daylight and are easy to photograph there. Many mammals regularly visit garbage cans around camps and country places, so it would be easy to lure them in front of the camera with food, a salt block, or a pool of water. Members of the weasel family, and opossums and raccoons are easily attracted. They set off the preset camera flash by pulling at bait or by touching a trip wire. This may mean leaving one's camera out overnight but if it is covered with a plastic refrigerator bag with a hole cut out in front of the lens, no harm should come to it.

Larger animals such as deer, bear, moose, and elk, can be stalked. This takes skill and a knowledge of the animal's habits. One of the additional benefits of nature photography is that much of interest is learned about the subject one is photographing. National parks, where the larger mammals have been protected for many years, offer the greatest variety of opportunities for the nature photographer.

Because most animals are cautious and always on the move, a camera with a fast shutter is best; also a longer than normal focal length lens, to get larger images at a distance. A fast film should be used because one will be shooting at higher speeds and also because few animals are found in bright sunlight.

Insects and Other Small Subjects

The rhinocerous beetle, the praying mantis, or even the common garden spider are bizarre and interesting as possible photographic subjects. There are more species of insects than all other forms of animal life and some can be found almost anywhere except in salt water. Generally they are easier to photograph than birds or mammals.

For color, butterflies should be considered; for strange shapes, beetles and bugs; for delicateness, the damselflies. Busy ants excavating a tunnel, or a spider weaving a delicate web are absorbing subjects.

For this work a camera should have extension tubes or bellows in order to give large magnification. Through-the-lens viewing or ground-glass focusing (like that of a press camera or view camera) enables one to focus sharply and compose the picture precisely. Some cameras, without extension bellows or tubes and through-the-lens focusing, can be used if one is careful in measuring the exact distance and makes adjustment for parallax.

Since many insects make regular visits to certain flowers, focus, exposure, composition, and lighting can be set before taking the picture. For instance, if one finds a fresh milkweed flower, the camera can be set up and the right butterfly, sphinx moth, or bumblebee to come along. One can even set a background of cloth or colored cardboard behind the flower.

A tripod is essential when shooting at such close distances. Stopping the lens down as far as possible to $f.$ 11, $f.$ 16, or $f.$ 22, will help to assure sufficient depth of field. Use of a cable release will prevent moving the camera when snapping the picture.

Plants

Though plants do not move about as do birds, insects and other animals, they do present a challenge. Large trees, for example, are hard to find as perfect, isolated specimens. Most are heavier on one side or are crowded by others or

A front view of a photographer's blind (top) and a back view (bottom) shows a method by which wildlife can be photographed at close range

found growing on hillsides where the photographer will have difficulty working. Their immobility is as much of a problem as the mobility of the animals. However, the ingenious photographer, by using the right combination of camera, lenses, and viewpoint, can surmount these difficulties—or he can keep searching until he finds the right tree.

For many botanical subjects, a view or press type camera can be used. The subjects can be focused and composed through the ground glass. A single tree or smaller plant photographed against the sky or an artificial background is very effective. For many smaller plants, artificial light is an aid. Sometimes in deep woods or shadows, it is a necessity. Fortunately one has time to adjust his camera and lights for the best possible picture. Some photographers prefer available-light pictures; others, time exposures for the more natural effect they give.

Plants that appear dry and dusty can be livened by using a spray of water and glycerine. Mix about 1 part of glycerine to 15 parts of water and shake well. Just before taking the picture, spray a fine mist over leaves and flower. This will bring out the color and make the plant look much fresher and greener.

Seeds and fruits of plants make as interesting pictures as do leaves, flowers, or complete plants. Extreme close-ups of stamens and other floral parts rarely seen at close range always enliven a sequence of plant pictures.

Reptiles and Amphibians

For turtles and snakes sunning on logs or rocks near water, artificial light is not necessary, but dwellers in the deep woods are best photographed with supplementary light. Frogs and toads may be brought back and photographed in a terrarium. Salamanders, lizards, and snakes are more mobile and require more patience and understanding.

Fishes

Photographing fishes in their natural habitat requires more than just a camera. A water-tight camera case is necessary. It must have a shutter release and perhaps a film winding knob, focusing knob, and an aperture setting control. Where one can legally do so, smaller fishes can be caught and placed in a small aquarium where they can be more easily photographed. If it is possible, take a small glass tank to the seashore, net small ones, photograph them and return them to the water—all within a short time. This should be done under an umbrella or other shade so that the lighting can be controlled, and reflections from the glass reduced.

Summary

Anyone sincerely interested in the welfare of wildlife and devoted to its preservation will conscientiously avoid endangering the life of any subject he is trying to photograph. He will pass up a chance to get a rare picture if it involves misrepresenting the subject or injuring it.

Many improvised or faked pictures have appeared in print but the experienced naturalist usually can distinguish them at a glance. To get genuine satisfaction from his hobby of nature photography, the real sportsman sets his standards high. He must never be ashamed of the methods he uses to get his pictures.

Finally, he will look upon his pictures not only as trophies of a bloodless chase but as a means of conveying to others the fascination of nature and the need for understanding and appreciating the value of wildlife resources.   —H.W.K.

Recommended Reading

The Complete Book of Nature Photography—Russ Kinne. Ziff Davis, New York.
Guide to Photographing Animals—Sam Dunton. Greenberg Publishers, New York.
Hunting with the Camera—Allan D. Cruickshank, Charles E. Mohr, Edward S. Ross, Herman W. Kitchen, and Rutherford Platt. Harper & Brothers, New York.
Nature Photography Guide—Herbert D. Shumway. Greenberg Publishers, New York.

NATURE QUIZ
Electrical Nature Games

Electrical nature games teach recognition, by pictures, of the common plants and animals that live around one, and in doing so, make a game of it. They are good preparation for going into the field and provide fun and interest for persons of all ages.

Briefly the quiz game consists of a board on which pictures of birds, flowers, or other natural objects have been mounted. In one corner the names of all the items pictured are listed. On the back of the board a wire connects an electrical contact beside each picture with the contact beside its name. When one of two metal pointers (both wired to a battery and light or buzzer) is touched to the metal button beside a picture and the second pointer touches the metal button beside its name, a light flashes or buzzer sounds telling the operator he has named the picture correctly.

These boards are relatively inexpensive and are so simple to make that children can do all the building of them by themselves.

Bird Namer

One of the most popular electrical quiz games is the *bird namer*. To make this you will need:

A board of convenient size (30 by 40 inches suggested)—3-ply wood is light and easy to handle and various pressed woods are satisfactory too.

Pictures of birds: The National Audubon Society has published 4 sets of pictures, 50 each, postcard size (spring, summer, winter and western birds). For smaller pictures, use bird stamps in inexpensive children's books, or the stamps of the National Wildlife Federation, Washington, D.C., or two sets of 15 Useful Birds of America (published by Church & Dwight Company, Inc., 70 Pine St., New York, New York.)

Some people like to be able to change the pictures from time to time, perhaps

Using a bird namer children learn to identify birds at a trailside museum

using a different set of 50 birds, or using mammals, flowers, trees. To do this, trim all pictures to one size, or if necessary mount on cards cut to one size and attach to board with photographic art corners or by strips of wood or metal molding. The pictures are then easily interchangeable.

Names of birds: These should be printed in large bold letters. Arrange alphabetically and allow approximately one inch between the base of one name and the base of the name next below it.

Brass paper fasteners: These are the electrical contacts. Get 1-inch paper fasteners (Dennison supplies these in boxes of 100, or see your stationery or office supply store). You will need one fastener for each picture and one for each name.

Bell wire: This is single strand copper wire with plastic insulation. It is usually sold in coils of 25, 50, 75, and 100 feet. The amount needed will depend on the size of the board, the number of pictures and the position of the names (whether in the center or far to one side).

Tools: A drill, with bit the same diameter as the width of the prongs on the paper fastener, to make a hole beside each picture and each name; wire snips or old scissors to cut the wire to needed lengths; pliers, preferably the long-nosed type, to curl under the prongs of the paper fasteners and hold the wire tightly; yardstick to help with the layout of the pictures.

Since the battery, light or buzzer, and pointers are not a part of the board but comprise a separate unit for use with many boards, these will be treated later, after the board is made.

To Make the Board
1. First sandpaper the edges and corners until smooth, and clean surface of board with sandpaper or eraser if necessary. Paint or use natural finish.
2. Binding edges with colored tape gives a neat, finished appearance, like a frame, and protects the edges from soil and chipping.
3. Lay out entire board with pictures and names. Suggestion: Leave a vacant rectangle at top center where lights or buzzer may be hooked on. Be sure pictures are thoroughly mixed, that is, in a different order from their names. Use yardstick to help obtain neat arrangement and mount pictures and names.
4. Use yardstick again to mark places for contacts beside each picture and each name. Placing these one under the other in neat rows gives a trim appearance. Drill the holes. Insert the paper fasteners and open out the prongs enough to hold. The board is now ready to wire.

5. Two or four persons can work at this together. First person takes coil of wire and, on front of board, pulls out enough to reach from contact beside first name in list to contact by its picture. Allow two inches extra for twisting about contacts and cut. Second person with knife or scissors removes insulation from one inch at either end of this wire. Third person, standing behind board, makes the attachment with assistance from fourth person who shows him which contact to use by wiggling these on the front of the board. The attachment is made by twisting the bare ends of the wire snugly around the prongs of the paper fastener and then curling the ends of the prong under. Special care must be taken where contacts are fairly close, as in the list of names, to be sure prongs of one contact do not touch those of any other as this could give a wrong answer. Meanwhile the first person has measured off another length of wire. This procedure continues until the board is wired. When finished, the back of the board will be a maze of crisscrossing wires. The board is now finished and ready to use.

The Electrical Unit.
   You will need:
   Battery: One 6-volt battery, the type used for a lantern flashlight is excellent. Two of the large dry cell (doorbell) batteries may also be used.

   Buzzer or doorbell: Remember these are noisy and while good attention getters when used at a fair or a bazaar, most teachers, librarians, parents, museum workers prefer noiseless flashing lights.
   Lights: Get two flashlight bulbs of suitable size to operate on your battery (ask your dealer).
   Wires: Get five feet of lamp wire, the flat rubber type, with the two insulated wires easily separable. Several feet of bell wire, the same as that used to wire the chart.

FRONT VIEW

Pointer

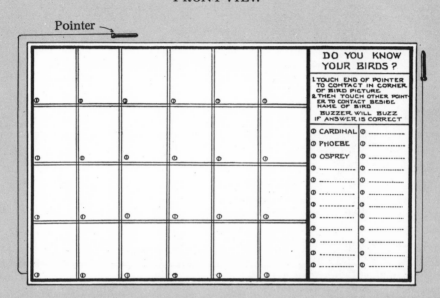

DO YOU KNOW
YOUR BIRDS?

1. TOUCH END OF POINTER
   TO CONTACT IN CORNER
   OF BIRD PICTURE.
2. THEN TOUCH OTHER POINT-
   ER TO CONTACT BESIDE
   NAME OF BIRD.
   BUZZER WILL BUZZ
   IF ANSWER IS CORRECT

CARDINAL
PHOEBE
OSPREY

DIAGRAM OF CONNECTIONS

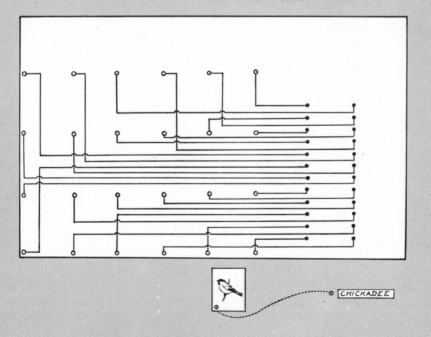

CHICKADEE

The electrical connections of a bird namer can be varied as desired. The basic principle is to connect the name of the bird with its picture

Board: Small square of plywood board for mounting buzzer or lights.

Other Items: Coping saw to cut out a "wise" owl or "clever" fox whose flashlight bulb-eyes will blink for the right answer; clothespin to glue on back of owl or fox or buzzer board to clip it on the chart; solder and soldering iron to attach wires to flashlight bulbs; two short lengths of brass rod to serve as pointers; tape or solder to join wire to rods; two 6 by 1 by 1 inch lath to serve as handles for the pointers.

To Make the Electrical Unit

Buzzer or doorbell: Mount on plywood board with screws provided, attach a short length of bell wire to each contact. Glue clothespin on back to clamp over top of chart in space provided.

Lights: Draw outline of owl or fox on plywood and cut out with coping saw; hollow out eyes to size to hold flashlight bulbs securely and let stems project behind. Paint or crayon owl or fox. Glue clothespin on back side to clip on top of chart in space provided. Remove insula-

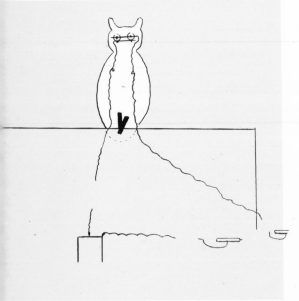

Based on the same principle as a bird namer, an owl's eyes light up when the correct answer is touched with a pointer

tion from three or four inches of short length bell wire (enough to reach from base of one flashlight bulb to base of second) and attach to each base with drop of solder. Remove insulation from three or four inches of second short length of wire and place against solder spot on stem of each flashlight bulb and solder in place.

Pointers: Pull halves of lamp wire apart, making two five-feet lengths of many strand insulated copper wire. Remove insulation from one inch at end of each wire and from three inches at opposite end. Drill a hole through a five-inch dowel handle using a bit a little smaller than the diameter of the rod pointer. Twist the exposed copper strand wire tightly and thread through dowel handle. Solder wire to end of brass rod and pull back into handle leaving an inch or two of rod extending from the end of the handle to make contact with the paper fasteners. Rod should fit firmly in handle.

Hang chart on wall in position to use. Clip light or sound board on top. Use bell wire to connect one of wires from lights or sound to end of pointer wire at midpoint of one side. Place screw hook on edge of board at this point and give pointer wire one turn around it to prevent pull on wire connected to sound or lights. Place battery in position (on floor beneath board), on nearby shelf, or suspend (inside small bag) from wall and connect second wire from light or sound board to one pole of battery with strand of bell wire. Run bell wire from second pole of battery to midpoint of other side of chart, connect with second pointer and loop once around a screw hook to prevent pull on battery. The board is now ready to use. Place one pointer on contact beside first name in list and second pointer against contact beside picture name represents. Lights should flash or buzzer sound.

Varients of the *Bird Namer* might be *Tree Namer, Wild Flower Namer, Mammal Namer, Fish Namer.* Children can easily make their own pictures for the *Tree Namer* by making leaf prints (crayon, stamp pad, blue print, ozalid print) of their leaves (*See Nature Craft Projects*). Winter twigs of trees are easily attached to file cards with scotch tape and mounted on nature chart. Seeds may be glued to cards or placed in plastic vials and these attached to cards for mounting. Shells, small rocks, and mineral specimens are other interesting subjects.

Nature electrical games can be made on a single large sheet of scrapbook paper. Children confined to beds or wheelchairs enjoy these. Small pictures must be used here. Names listed need not be more than one-half inch apart. Arrange page and paste on pictures and names. Place page over old board for protection while holes are being made. Use large nailset for hole making. Place end of nailset where hole is to be made and give one sharp blow with a hammer; a neat round hole will result. The hole is the contact this time. Cut narrow strips of paper-backed aluminum foil — to use instead of wires. On back of chart sheet connect hole by picture with hole by its name using a strip of the paper-backed foil. Stick down over both holes with short piece of scotch tape. Be sure foil is paper-backed. The paper provides the insulation. The foil side should be turned toward the back of the chart so that the foil shows in the hole. When page is "wired" with the strips of paper-backed foil, clip lights or buzzer board to edge of scrapbook and use pointers as before. Many foods (cereals and mixes) are packaged with paper-backed aluminum foil, a convenient source of this material.

Several quiz games can be set up in one scrapbook.

True or False Chart

Mount a series of printed statements, some true, some false, on board. Place brass paper fastener contact beside each statement. Connect contacts beside all true statements together with bell wire.

Bird namers can be devised to hold several sets of bird cards such as those available from the National Audubon Society

Do the same for all false statements. Place two lights at top of board in holes drilled to hold stem tightly. Print the word, *true*, under one light and the word *false*, under the other. Run a wire from nearest true statement to true light, remove insulation from half-inch at end of wire and force into hole tight against stem of true light. Do the same to connect nearest false statement with false light. Remove insulation from about three inches of bell wire and solder to bases of two lights. Connect this wire to one pole of your battery. Run a second wire from other pole of battery to side of chart and connect pointer (made as for *Bird Namer*). Whenever pointer touches contact beside a statement, the appropriate light (*true* or *false*) will go on.

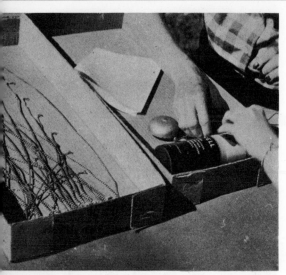

Portable quiz units can be made out of cardboard containers

Nest Chart

Draw or paint a composite picture showing nesting sites of common birds. Place pictures of these birds at top of chart. Connect contacts beside each bird with contact by its nesting site.

Area Chart

Make a picture map of your camp or sanctuary area. Around the map mount pictures or drawings of nests, trees, flowers, springs, rock formations one wishes to call attention to. Wire contact beside each picture to contact by its location on the map. Children and visitors using this chart will learn where to look for interesting items shown on board.

Habitat Chart

Make a composite picture showing various habitats — fields, woodlands, marshes, pond, shore. Place bird pictures at top. Wire contact beside each bird picture to contact in its preferred nesting habitat. Several birds may be wired to one habitat contact.   —D.A.T.

NATURE STUDY (*See Children and Nature*)

NATURE TRAIL
How to Build a Nature Trail

Every national park has nature trails. Many state, county, and municipal parks have them too. Each summer more and more of them are established in camps, and an increasing number of schools are laying out trails as part of their program for expanding education beyond the classroom.

Planning and setting up a labeled trail is an exciting and worthwhile project because in the process a lot of exploration goes on, a lot of surprising things are discovered, and a way for thousands of other people to learn about the fascinating world of nature. A nature trail can help make people better citizens and more understanding custodians of natural resources.

Few people walking through the woods are aware of many of the things in full view, let alone those features that require an attentive or discerning eye. Even the trained naturalist overlooks much of interest because he is momentarily preoccupied, distracted, or otherwise unobservant.

But observations drawn from many trips and from naturalists of rich and varied backgrounds — when eloquently expressed and skillfully presented in booklet or label form—can make any piece of landscape glow with meaning. This selection of meaningful sites, "stations" at which one can pause, observe, and comprehend, is the role of the nature trail.

The trailside story—the information and inspiration presented — is always available. It serves as a tireless, ever-present guide. There is almost no limit to the number of persons who can participate happily in trail tours—certainly infinitely more than could hope for personalized tours.

Certainly one is interested in doing more than simply cataloging the plants, the geological features, and the more common, obvious animals that may be seen with some regularity. People quickly become bored with *names*—or they soon forget them. But boys, particularly, will remember that wood from an ash tree is used for making baseball bats and tennis racquets.

Why the Trail Idea Works

Nature trails are interesting because people are likely to discover new things about more or less familiar objects, stories of interrelationships, often unsuspected. The value of dead tree trunks in building up the humus; the way humus acts as a sponge in holding rainwater, releasing it gradually, reducing wasteful runoff.

They alert people to things that are happening— or example, that sun-loving bayberries, sumacs, apple trees, and red cedars are dying where faster-growing forest trees are spreading a parasol of leaves over them, shutting out the sunlight.

One gets a new insight into past events. He learns farmers once tilled the land that is now wooded. Stone walls, eroded gullies, and other evidence prove it.

Even the future can be predicted in a forest by noting which, if any, seedlings are present. As one species replaces another the changing food supply will eliminate some forms of animal life in favor of ones better adapted to the new community.

Sometimes there are stories with surprise endings, like the one which tells how skunks control the number of turtles in an area (by eating their eggs). As a result more wood ducks survive (fewer snapping turtles to eat the young ducks).

If so much of interest can be revealed through a nature trail, one probably will say, "Let's get to work!" Now it must be decided where to put it, how to select things to be labeled, and what to say about them.

Locating the Best Route

1. Accessibility. Whether in camp, public park, or sanctuary, the entrance to the

Nature trail signs should tell the visitor what to expect, something about the area, the theme, and the length of the trail

trail should be conspicuous enough to attract attention. When practical, start from the interpretive center or other gathering place.

2. Route. To arouse the greatest interest the trail should have as much variety as possible. The plants and animals of a field differ from those of a woodland; a cool ravine is quite unlike a dry rocky ridge; a running stream and a swamp are surprisingly dissimilar. Try to include as many different habitats as possible.

3. Length. This will depend on the size of the available area, the terrain, and the distribution of interesting features. A good length is about one-half mile. Well-labeled, it may keep a visitor looking

Nature trails help create the feeling of more personal exploration than do road-like routes

and learning for an hour.

Most trails are designed as loop or figure-eight layouts. They bring the visitor back approximately to the starting point so no extra walking is involved on the return trip. The figure-eight permits the visitor to go over the whole trail or settle for half of it.

In a camp or park a trail may utilize a fairly short existing path connecting two important areas. Or a few stations may be set up along an extensive hiking trail.

On the White Oak Canyon Nature Trail, in Shenandoah National Park, Virginia, seven widely spaced stations were so situated that some significant landscape feature could be sighted, usually through a peephole drilled near the top of a head-high post. A conspicuous label answered the question, "What is happening?" and another. "What is the effect?"

How to Select the Features

As soon as the major areas to be visited have been tentatively agreed upon, expert advice will prove useful in selecting the specific features. Persons well versed in natural history should be invited to go over the area.

If they clearly understand what one is trying to do, these experts can help find lots of fine features: very large trees and ones with contrasting bark; squirrels' nests and probable dens; springs and clear-running brooks; picturesque rock outcrops; lichens, mosses, pockets of ferns, and wild flowers.

Get a fisherman to point out what makes a trout stream productive.

A lumberman or a forest service technician can help set up trailside explanations of forest management and utilization—how to scale timber, what a cord of wood is, or a board foot.

Marking the Trail

1. Mark conspicuously and number tentatively the features which the experts consider noteworthy.

2. Compile a list, with the experts' remarks, for use later when labels are being prepared.

3. Lay out a tentative trail first with pieces of surveyor's brightly colored tape, and then with string to connect as many of these selected features as is feasible.

4. Revise the checklist so that items to be labeled are neither too closely bunched nor too far apart. Many unlabeled features can be included in guided tours, or in booklets prepared for trips at a different season.

5. Clear a footpath when satisfied that the route selected will cause the least disturbance to plantlife and will minimize natural hazards.

Needed: Foresight and Restraint

Consider carefully the long-range effect that continued use will have on the natural attractiveness of the area. Remember that:

Steep grades are tiring and result in erosion—so try to follow contour lines; zigzag as gradually as possible.

Straight-line trails are more monotonous, and hold less suspense than winding trails, but sharp corners invite shortcuts which soon produce a barren network of trampled trails. Where a maze of trails already exist use ingenuity to hide them with natural debris and by planting ferns and appropriate shrubs or trees.

Seasonal wet spots or floods may make the trail impassable and force destructive detours. Provide raised footpaths or convenient stepping stones. Areas of this sort may be extremely interesting, so don't avoid them.

Broad, roadlike routes are the antithesis of the nature trail idea. A narrow footpath creates an atmosphere suggestive of exploration, distant from the exhausting hubbub of the city. This feeling of remoteness is lost as the trail becomes wider. Take advantage of terrain, boulders, fallen tree trunks and branches to unobtrusively channel visitors within the narrow confines of the trail.

Subjects for Labels

Since the visitor needs to get acquainted with the conspicuous features in a habitat, labels for trees, shrubs, wild flowers, and other plants usually outnumber other subjects.

The story of plant succession and other ecological features can be presented simply on most trails. The geological story also can be dramatized, particularly where there is fossil or glacial evidence of past events.

With birds, mammals, insects, and other forms of animal life, labels may be used to alert the visitor to the fact that he has entered a specific habitat where, for example, the Louisiana waterthrush nests and is likely to be seen. Or it explains which mammals are nocturnal in habit, others that might be seen in the daytime.

Teamwork Produces Good Labels

Two heads or more are better than one when it comes to writing labels or signs. The best way is to have several persons read up on each topic to be covered and each write a label. Then compare notes and incorporate the best features into one label.

A dash of imagination and originality of expression helps. So does final editing by someone "stingy with words," who can condense the idea into a few words. Make the label as chatty and friendly as possible.

This was one of the classic labels on the first well-known nature trail, at Bear Mountain, in Palisades Interstate Park, New York:

Happy are cicadas' lives
For they all have voiceless wives.

A familiar object or expression used in an unexpected situation is guaranteed to stop traffic. Along the Audubon Nature Center trail at Greenwich, Connecticut, a red *Stop* sign focused attention on poison ivy. *Soft Shoulders* suggested that visitors would avoid trampling down the soft humus and killing ferns and wild flowers if they stayed on the path.

Don't Tell Everything

Advertising copywriters have learned that unless ideas are presented briefly most persons will not read ads. The hardest job in label writing is in keeping them short. To catch the attention of the mildly interested or disinterested person one must arouse his curiosity and alert him to what is around him. He is more likely to read a number of short signs than even a few long ones.

Longer labels may be included at intervals, particularly on trails where visitors are likely to have some knowledge of nature or where they return at intervals.

Leaflets can include more information than signs, but they too, must be written with style and brevity.

Imaginative use of illustrations and designs adds greatly to the appeal of the trail. Sometimes the key numbers are printed on a leaf design, or on a footprint.

Once copy for the label has been written, suitable materials must be chosen. If the nature trail is located in a camp, inexpensive temporary labels will be adequate. Some camps and most park and sanctuary trails use more permanent signs made of masonite, wood, metal, or plastic.

Temporary Labels

A good grade shipping tag such as Dennison's 5 GC green, 4¾ by 2¼ inches, can be dipped in varnish, or sprayed with clear plastic Krylon after lettering. Tie to a twig, or tack to a rustic stake at the edge of the trail. Larger labels, of waterproof paper or cardboard, can be tacked or glued to a board.

Green tags, "Talking Leaves," are used by the hundreds at Westmoreland Sanctuary, Bedford, New York, but since they are used strictly for blooming of wild flowers and other features of brief duration, there are never too many on the trail at any one time.

Cards or tags dipped in melted paraffin often last through a full camping season. File cards 4 by 6 or 5 by 8 inches are quite suitable and lend themselves to brief, catchy messages and cartoonlike sketches, outlines of leaves, track patterns, and other simple illustrations. Remember that paraffin is inflammable and should be melted in a double boiler.

Competition among camp units in preparing signs can be highly instructive and enjoyable.

Tags are well adapted for the question-and-answer technique—the question on one side, the answer on the reverse:

1. What earthly good is a centipede?
1. One has one leg up on this ques-

tion if he can answer: What good are you?

Superpermanent Labels

Where supervision can be provided and traffic controlled, more elaborate and expensive signs may be warranted. Sturdy supports are necessary. More or less absent-mindedly, children and occasionally, adults, lean on signs, "worry" them loose, and in prankish mood, turn them backward or interchange them with other signs.

A "deadman"—a spike or rod running at right angles to the stake—buried well below ground, discourages attempts at removal.

Rustic stakes are more appropriate than pipes, dowels, or other milled lumber, but forests should not be raided to get material for this purpose. Cypress, locust, or cedar will outlast spruce stakes but even spruce serves for years if soaked in "penta" or other preservative.

Where stakes without deadmen are used, drive the hole with a crowbar to avoid damaging the stake by pounding it.

The signs themselves can be made on waterproof paper and mounted on a wooden block or frame (routed out to a depth of ¼ to ½ inch) or on thin sheet aluminum by hand-lettering, printing, or photo-offset processes. Or the signs may be lettered directly on:

Wood. Locust or pine are most often chosen. Signs 6 by 8 or 8 by 10 inches provide space enough for lettering and yet aren't large enough to clutter the landscape.

Where wayside exhibits of more comprehensive scope are located along a trail, marine plywood in sizes up to 30 by 36 inches may be utilized. Wooden signs in all sizes may be covered with fiberglass—by the same process used to cover the hulls of boats. This greatly increases the life expectancy of the sign. In the Forest Preserve of Cook County, Illinois, fiberglass covered signs have survived five years of use with virtually no deterioration.

Composition board. Tempered masonite is more short-lived, and more subject to warping than ¼-inch lumber but is suitable material for signs. It will look better and last longer if given a base coat of outdoor paint or auto enamel.

Plastics. Heavy grade vinyl plastic, available in green, white, and some other colors, when lettered with paints made for use on plastics proves a very satisfactory material. Larger sizes should be mounted on wood.

Laminated plastic preferably in flexible sheets, can be inscribed on machines made for that purpose and produce the familiar signs of office and laboratory. For more formal labeling, in botanic gardens, zoos, and municipal parks, they are attractive, legible, and remarkably durable.

Lettering the Signs

Quite professional lettering can be done with a stylus guided by a draughtsman's lettering set. The Leroy set (distributed by Keuffel and Esser, 127 Fulton Street, New York City) is expensive but is widely used. Several labels can be lettered side by side if a frame is built to the same thickness as the labels.

Original illustrations done in ink or with oil paints, add much interest to signs. As a substitute, low cost children's books are a source of many excellent pictures. They can be glued to wood or metal and varnished or covered with fiberglass.

An Alternative to Signs—Leaflets

Generally the visitor to a national park nature trail has an opportunity to borrow a copy of an interpretive leaflet for use as he travels along the trail. When he gets back to the starting point he may return the leaflet to the rack, or deposit a small fee and keep the bulletin.

About half of the visitors buy them. That way they have an accurate refer-ence to the natural history of the area, and an attractive, useful memento of their tour.

Several hundred leaflets have been prepared in the last few years. Improvement in makeup and content has been notable, while cost has been kept remarkably low by heavy sales. In price they range from simple fold-over mimeographed leaflets costing about one cent apiece to handsome letterpress and offset publications with natural color photographs, which sell for a quarter or less.

A packet of outstanding leaflets has been assembled by the Association of Interpretive Naturalists and is now available to the public.

Educational Use of Trails

Since nature trails represent routes carefully selected for variety of wildlife habitat and natural interest they generally provide the best areas for guided tours.

If the trail has been laid out with such use in mind there will be some assembly points where a group of 20 or more persons can gather around the tour leader. In the national parks, groups as large as 100 can be assembled at certain points.

A variety of lettering devices are available for making signs for nature trails

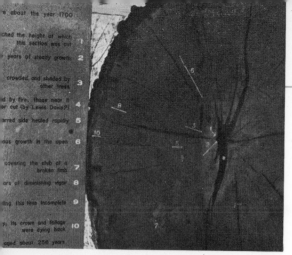

Local events and growing conditions can be keyed to tree rings

When a class is conducted over a nature trail, the labels or leaflet copy may be (1)ignored, (2) featured, (3) amplified, or (4) debated.

Due to the unwieldliness of the group there probably will not be time to stop at more than a few of the stations. The larger the group, the fewer the stops.

To promote further, future use of the leaflet it is well to specifically discuss some of the items, pointedly calling attention to wording, illustrations, references, or other features.

To adapt the trail to different age groups or to selected subject fields, the visiting group can be instructed to concentrate on certain specified numbers, or labels designated by plastic tape of a particular color, encircling the stake.

Single mimeographed sheets with "Twenty Questions" to be answered from information on color-coded labels help make self-guided tours more effective.

But trailside information of this sort is less important than developing an appreciation of the wonder and beauty of the out-of-doors, and the importance of setting aside and protecting from damage and overuse, choice samples of our natural heritage.

Imaginative use of nature trails can help enlist support for the organizations and agencies that are promoting preservation of natural areas.

Community cooperation is important at every stage: Planning, building, use, and maintenance. The more persons and organizations that have had a part in it, the greater will be the interest and support. But one group must have major responsibility for the trail, to insure its permanence. —C.E.M.

Testing trails stimulate a young naturalist to propose some answers of his own

Trailside bulletin boards are used for exhibits, announcements, and other information of interest

Recommended Reading

Bulletins in Park Management Series: No. 5, Nature Trail Labels; No. 6, Outdoor Education for Better Living; No. 7, Interpretive Programs. American Institute of Park Executives, Oglebay Park, Wheeling, West Virginia.

Enjoying Nature: Nature Centers, Nature Trails, and Trailside Museums—Reynold E. Carlson. National Recreation Association, New York.

Handbook for Teaching of Conservation and Re-
source-use—Richard L. Weaver. The Interstate
Printers and Publishers, Danville, Illinois.
Interpreting Our Heritage—Freeman Tilden, Uni-
versity of North Carolina Press, Chapel Hill,
North Carolina.
Packet of Selected Nature Trail Leaflets. Asso-
ciation of Interpretive Naturalists, Kalamazoo
Nature Center, Kalamazoo, Michigan.

NAUTILUS

The nautiluses are the only living
cephalopods with shells (*See Cephalopod*). The several species of nautilus
are found in the warm, southeast Asian
oceans. As with the other cephalopods,
nautiluses are carnivorous, living on
small forms of animal life that they
catch with their many tentacles.

The shell of the nautilus is a perfectly
formed spiral. It is divided into many
compartments, each proportionate in
size to its distance from the apex. The
animal resides in the last and largest
compartment. While alive, a thin layer
of organic material covers the shell; the
colorful exterior, and the pearly interior
of marketed shells usually have been
enhanced by acids.

In its normal habitat the nautilus
lives on the ocean floor, crawling about
in search of crustaceans and other animals upon which it feeds. Sick or damaged individuals are often found floating
on the surface of the ocean buoyed up
by the gases in their empty compartments (*See also under Mollusk*). —G.B.S.

NAVIGATION (*See under Animal: Nav -
igation of Animals by Sun and Stars*)

NEMOPHILA
Other Common Names— Baby blue-eyes
Scientific Name— *Nemophila menziesii*
Family—Hydrophyllaceae (waterleaf
family)
Range—California from Mendocino and
Shasta counties to San Diego County
Habitat—Open moist flats and slopes at
low altitudes, Upper Sonoran and Trans-
ition Zones
Time of Blooming—February to June

Nemophila

The blue in this flower is very soft
and the fresh white center is often dotted
with purple. One relative, called fiesta
flower, half climbs over shrubs and has
flowers of deep purple. Another has
orange-red flowers and is called fiddle-
neck—the buds being coiled at the tip
and looking like the neck of a fiddle.
Rock phacelia, with purple flowers,
travels from coast to high mountains.
Giant phacelia, with bluish-purple flowers, is from two to three feet high. Its
juice makes a stain like iodine.

NENE
Other Common Names—Hawaiian goose
Scientific Name—*Branta sandwichensis*
Family—Anatidae (swans, geese, and
ducks)
Order—Anseriformes
Size—Length, 26 inches
Range—The Hawaiian Islands

Saving the Hawaiian Nene

Saving from extinction the world's scarcest wildfowl, the Hawaiian goose, *Branta sandwichensis*, has been the object of a project in the state of Hawaii. This attempt to protect and breed the rare bird, called nene (nay-nay) by the Hawaiians, was begun by the Territorial Board of Agriculture and Forestry and engaged the attention of ornithologists and wildlife biologists around the world.

Charles W. Schwartz, wildlife biologist formerly connected with the Board of Agriculture, seems to have been the first to suggest a practical method of saving the nene from extinction. In his book, *The Game Birds of Hawaii*, published in 1949, he pointed out that although the bird had been protected by law for more than 20 years, this protection was not sufficient to give much hope that it could increase in the wild, due to food scarcity, attacks by predators, and some illegal hunting. He proposed that the board set up a controlled experiment with captive birds under the best possible conditions and carry on a careful study that might lead to the nene's restoration in considerable numbers. The project was set up at Pohakuloa, on the slopes of Maona Kea island of Hawaii.

The Pohakuloa project (the name means *big rock* in Hawaiian) was begun by the Board in August 1949, with the loan of two pairs of adult nenes from Herbert Shipman of Hilo, who owned the last flock of any size. To these were added one from Kapiolani Zoo in Honolulu and one captured in the wild. This latter bird was caught by a hunter who was met and relieved of it by a game warden, who recognized it as a rare nene and brought it to the project.

Soon after the decision to begin the study had been made, J. Donald Smith of the Board of Agriculture, Fish and Game Division, wrote to several wildlife authorities in various places, for information and suggestions that might be helpful. He found them much interested and anxious to be of assistance. Peter Scott, director of the Severn Wildfowl Trust, Slimbridge, in England, offered to send John J. Yealland, curator of Birds at the Severn Wildfowl Trust, to Hawaii. The offer was eagerly accepted. Captain Jean Delacour of the American Museum of Natural History, New York City, also expressed great interest in the project and gave much valuable advice.

Meanwhile things were going well for the nenes at Pohakuloa. One of the Shipman pairs mated, and a normal clutch of four eggs was laid. One of these was accidentally broken, and found to be fertile, which was exciting news, since eggs laid by captive wild geese often are not. Yealland arrived in time to observe the hatching on February 5, 1950, of two healthy goslings, and spent about two months helping with their care and sketching them and their parents from time to time. When he left he took with him one pair of adults to add to the Severn Trust, which needed only three species to complete its collection of all living wildfowl of the world.

Anxious to find out why the third egg did not hatch, Smith sent it to the New York State College of Agriculture at Ithaca, New York. It was examined by Alexis Romanoff, outstanding oologist, whose opinion was that the failure might have been caused by poor nutrition, and also that it was not surprising, since early death of the embryo is not uncommon in the eggs of birds laid in captivity.

The nene is extremely fastidious in its mating habits. Mated pairs show definite connubial affection, and go through a period of courtship before and during the laying of eggs, in which the male bows and dips elaborately as a sign of his devotion.

At this time the gander becomes extremely pugnacious, and will attack other males if not kept away from them. He is very attentive to his mate during the incubation and should anything happen to her he will take over the job. In fact, Shipman relates that one of his geese once left her nest for a night, only to be killed next morning by her angry mate, which then finished raising the family. The parents show great affection toward their offspring, too, and when strangers approach the family they assume a protective attitude, with ruffled plumage and extended necks.

Most of the birds at the Pohakuloa project came originally from the Shipman ranch, Puuwaawaa, on the slopes of Mt. Hualalai. Shipman, who probably knew more about the nene than anyone in Hawaii, said they develop attachments to particular people, as cats or dogs will. He tells of one goose that became so devoted to the elder Mrs. Shipman that when she drove from her home to Hilo, a distance of three or four miles, it would follow her, making the round trip on foot. The geese sometimes are extraordinarily fond of larger animals, too, like the one that chose a bull for its companion, and followed its bovine friend wherever he went around the ranch.

The Territorial Board of Agriculture had a threefold aim in conducting this study: first, to determine if possible the reasons for the disappearance of the nene; second, to establish a Hawaiian goose sanctuary in the wild when enough suitable range had been brought under its control; and third, when enough birds had been produced to make it feasible, to distribute pairs to selected aviaries and zoos, where the work of bringing back this almost extinct species might be carried on.

Such a project posed many problems. The nene, like all geese, matures very slowly, taking three years to attain breeding age. Breeding also is a slow process, since they lay from two to five eggs in a clutch, of which some usually fail to hatch, so that the increase in a flock would be much smaller than with

quail or pheasants, which produce from 10 to 15 young per year. Therefore the species cannot withstand the high mortality rate to which wild flocks were subjected with such disastrous effect.

Another problem was to provide sufficient feeding area. The nene feeds on the ground and needs a large area per bird. At Pohakuloa they were pastured on clover, which seems to take the place of the plants and berries that supplied the wild flocks in earlier times. This diet was supplemented by feedings of whole wheat, corn, barley, and a specially prepared mash, and the birds thrived on it. Since each bird needs approximately 2,500 square feet of space, the raising of any considerable number becomes expensive. Smith, who was in charge, estimated that a successful breeding project will cost about $185.00 per year per bird.

Like other birds that mature slowly, the nene has a very long life-span. One case is on record of a bird that was alive and healthy at the age of forty-two years. This patriarch was in Captain Delacour's aviary in Cleres, France, until the Germans took the country, and the collection of live birds, including the elderly Hawaiian goose, which was the last of its species in Europe. As he remarked in a letter to Smith, Captain Delacour often wondered how his forty-two-year-old fowl tasted, if it had ever reached the dinner table.

Paul Baldwin, wildlife biologist formerly at Hawaii National Park, and later with the University of California, published an intensive study of the nene. His bulletins, *The Hawaiian Goose, Its Distribution and Reduction in Numbers, The Condor,* Jan.-Feb. 1945 and *Foods of the Hawaiian Goose,* May-June 1947, record the story of the decline of this once abundant species, from an estimated 25,000 in the late 1700's to fewer than 50 birds in the early 1950's.

Though reduced to near-extermination, the nene was once plentifully distributed over the mountain slopes of the islands of Maui and Hawaii, and as late as 1891 were seen in fairly large numbers on the latter island. So far as is known, in the wild it seldom swam, and got the water it needed from the berries of the high, semi-arid slopes in summer and the soft plants of the lower lava flows where it went in winter to raise its young. From this adaptation it is believed that the webs of its feet have shrunken. They are only about half the size of those of other geese. The nene enjoys swimming in captivity, though Baldwin says it will drown in the open tanks provided for watering cattle.

Credit for saving the nene from complete extermination, in the opinion of Smith, should go chiefly to a few ranchers like Shipman, who kept small domesticated flocks after the wild birds had disappeared. Asked to account for the vanishing nene, Smith wrote:

"The disappearance of the nene is mysterious because no one knows exactly why this waterfowl should have become so scarce. All that we definitely know is that it is extraordinarily reduced in numbers compared to 'estimates' of its former population we have from the *haole* (white) adventurers of the 19th Century. We know that the nene is, among waterfowl, unique in its vulnerability to attacks by ground predators, particularly during the nesting and rearing seasons. In Hawaii there are not the marshes, lakes, and streams so characteristic of the natural range of the other geese of the world. The nene, therefore, after its appearance in Hawaii eons ago, had to become accustomed to a terrestrial existence. It was unfortunate that adaptability did not take arboreal lines. Rather, the Hawaiian goose became adapted to living among the lava flows and learned to eat the many types of fruits and herbs growing in the *Kipukas* (open, fertile spaces) on the volcanic slopes of the various cones found on Hawaii and Maui.

"In this phase of adaptability, the nene retained its natural habit of nesting on the ground. Tragically this placed the nest, the geese and the resulting flightless young in an extremely dangerous position after the introduction of the wild pig by the Polynesians, the dog and cat by both the natives and the white men, the mongoose, and many other foraging animals that inevitably followed the Caucasian invasion. The geese and the goslings in Hawaii do not have the opportunity of swimming away from predators as they can do in their northern nesting ranges. Here they must use their protective coloration and try to save themselves by hiding.

"There has, of course, been a great change in the vegetation of the Hawaiian Islands within the 19th and 20th centuries; however, there still remains much area on the island of Hawaii relatively unchanged by man. An abundance of food of the type that the nene is supposed to relish still exists in many of the *Kipukas* of Mauna Loa. Yet nenes have decreased just as sharply in these areas as along the coastlines. It does not seem possible that changes in the vegetation can be the most important cause of the reduction in numbers.

"My own opinion, and it is only that, concerning the causes of destruction is simply that the nene is extremely vulnerable to depredations during its nesting season. It is vulnerable to man, who has for centuries sought the goose for food. Although there has been a law forbidding the taking of nenes for many years, it has been relatively ineffective because of poor facilities for enforcement, the wide area of application, and ignorance on the part of the general public. The nene is vulnerable to predation by the wild pig, which even now literally plows up acres of the nene's former favorite nesting areas, and to attack by wild dogs which have no difficulty at all in wiping out entire families of geese during the breeding season. Of course, I could go on and list other predators, but the point is amply illustrated.

The nene has declined from an estimated 25,000 birds in the late 1700's to less than 50 birds in the early 1950's. It is now rigidly protected

"The only way in which we can restore the nene to even a semblance of its former numbers is by obtaining a large tract of land within the historic nene range and by diligent patrol to control the destructive factors which I have named. We have such a tract in mind and hope to be able to restock this area of Mauna Loa Forest and Game Reserve with the geese we are raising at Pohakuloa. Whether or not the problem is so simple of solution only time can answer; however, I am confident that with public understanding of the precarious status of the nene population and with sympathy toward our efforts to save it, we can actually restore a fairly large nucleus on the slopes of Mauna Loa within 20 years."

To those, and there are many in different parts of the world, who are interested in preserving rare wildfowl, this project, difficult and expensive as it is, seemed very important. Naturalists believed that this handsome goose, with its black, brown, and gray plumage and its distinctive spirally ruffled neck, has been the most neglected of all gamebirds, and hope that the preservation work will lead to the production of enough specimens so that some may be distributed to interested people who will carry on the work. Thus, hopefully, the nene will not join the large number of native Hawaiian birds that are now only pictures in books and stories told where old-timers gather to tell tales of the good old days in Hawaii. —N.B.E.

Unlike other geese, the nene is adapted to a terrestrial way of life

Status of the Nene in 1965

According to the Fish and Wildlife Service, United States Department of the Interior, the efforts of Hawaii and the United States Department of the Interior increased the number of the nene, or Hawaiian goose, Hawaii's state bird, from 25 to 60 (in 1948), to between 300 and 500 by January 1965. This is not considered adequate for the ultimate survival of the nene.

The nenes, both male and female, are grayish-brown. The top of the body is dark brown, the sides and belly are light brown, and the neck is creamy. Tail, wings, bill, and feet are black. Its feet are only partially webbed, a result of an adaptation (*see Adaptation of Birds*), because it has been away from water a long time. It lives on berries and greens. The goose lays four or five light brown eggs.

In 1948, when the Legislature of Hawaii appropriated $6,000 to help save the bird, there were only 13 in captivity and 12 to 50 in the wild. Hawaii's program included a study of the relationship between the nene and its environment, the setting aside of 8,100 acres as sanctuary, the breeding of captive birds, and the release of their offspring into former wild habitats.

In 1958, the Congress of the United States passed a bill authorizing the annual expenditure of $15,000 for a program of research, propagation, and the management necessary to effect the restoration of the nene to its natural habitat. The program is carried out by Hawaii's Department of Land and Natural Resources, under contract to the United States Department of the Interior's Bureau of Sport Fisheries and Wildlife.

In 1964, 37 goslings were reared. By 1964 a total of 150 geese had been released into the wild. Most of these birds were reared in the state's game farm, but 49 were supplied by the Wildfowl Trust in England. The action of the Wildfowl Trust was a case of birds being sent home to roost. The trust had received three birds from Hawaii in 1951 and had remarkable success in propagating them.

As of January 1965 there were between 300 and 500 nenes, more than half in captivity. The wild flock is located only on the islands of Hawaii and neighboring Maui. Only birds reared locally were released on Hawaii. Those released on Maui are considered insufficient in numbers to overcome the adverse factors that decimate the birds. The present Hawaii State game farm stock of 17 pairs cannot produce enough birds to make sure that the species will thrive (*See also Extinct and Threatened Animals of North America*).

Conservationists hope that additional sanctuaries can be provided for the nene. They believe that a restoration program, to be successful, must do the following: Modernize the propagation facilities to allow better handling of the captive stock; buy more space for sanctuaries; continue the control of predators, and develop the best combination of habitat factors to sustain a wild nene population of at least 500 birds on Maui and 500 on Hawaii.

Three nene were taken to the National Zoological Park in Washington D.C., in the spring of 1964. The zoo at this time was undergoing a major renovation, and signs informed visitors that "some animals will be housed in seemingly strange but temporary quarters." The nenes were temporarily in the house of the great cats—lions, tigers, leopards, jaguars, and panthers.　—J.K.T.

NEST AND NESTING (*See under Bird: Bird's Nests*)

NEWT

A newt is an amphibian belonging to the order of tailed amphibians, Urodela (or Caudata). Newts are mostly aquatic, but some of them go through an intermediate terrestrial (land-dwelling) stage during which they are commonly known as *efts*. While most aquatic salamanders have a slimy skin, the skin of a newt is somewhat rough. Newts are widely distributed throughout the eastern and central United States and Canada, the Pacific states, and also live in Europe, Africa, and Asia (*See Amphibian*).

Red-spotted Newt
Other Common Names — Eft, or red-spotted eft
Scientific Name — *Diemictylus viridescens*
Family — Salamandridae
Order — Urodela (or Caudata)
Size — Length, three to five inches

Range — Nova Scotia west to Great Lakes and south to Mississippi and Alabama

The red-spotted newt derives its name from the series of red spots that appear over most of its body, the basic color of which, in the adult, varies from brown to olive-green. They are commonly seen in ponds and even in the early spring can be seen swimming beneath the melting surface ice. After going through the larval aquatic stage, the red-spotted newt turns terrestrial, during which stage it is known as *red eft*, its color ranging from brilliant bright orange to dark red. Red efts can be found roaming the woodlands by the hundreds. However, despite their bright color and slow movements they are well protected against most predators, as they are capable of secreting from their skin glands a substance that has poisonous qualities to animals that might eat them. For example, a red eft was accidentally placed in a terrarium with a large Cuban tree frog, *Hyla*

Red-spotted newt

septentrionalis, that promptly swallowed it. A few seconds later the tree frog regurgitated the red eft, which walked away, seemingly none the worse for this experience. The Cuban tree frog went into convulsions and died within a few minutes.

The red eft stage of the red-spotted newt may last from two to three years after which time it usually darkens in color, adapts its shape for its new aquatic habitat, and reenters the water, where it will breed, and live out its remaining days.   —G.P.

NICTITATING MEMBRANE (*See under Adaptations of Birds*)

NIGHTHAWK
Common Nighthawk
Other Common Names—Bullbat, mosquito hawk
Scientific Name—*Chordeiles minor*
Family—Caprimulgidae (goatsuckers)
Order—Caprimulgiformes
Size—Length, 9 to 10 inches
Range—Breeds from Newfoundland south through Florida, and from the Yukon to Mexico

In late spring when the shade trees are in full leaf, the common nighthawk arrives in the city. Late in the afternoon or early evening the slender, slim-winged bird can be seen flying erratically about, high over the rooftops uttering its nasal call, a *peent* or *pee-ik*, a penetrating cry quite different from the calls of most other birds. Its long, slim wings are crossed by a broad, white bar toward the tip. This is the nighthawk's identification badge. The common nighthawk is between 8 to 10 inches long. Actually, the nighthawk is not a hawk at all, but belongs to the same family of birds as the whip-poor-will.

The common nighthawk is not so much a bird of the night as the whip-poor-will. Sometimes, even at midday, it will fly off its roost. Climbing upward with jerky, staggering wingbeats, it sud-

denly half folds its wings and plunges downward until it is just short of the roofs. At this moment, to avoid crashing, it levels off, and the wind, rushing through the stiff flight feathers, makes a loud rattling or booming sound, something like a gust of air on a large, loosely-stretched rubber band. The effect is very startling. The reason for the performance is to attract a mate.

The common nighthawk waits until the air is warm and plenty of insects are in the sky before it starts its long flight northward. The first ones reach Florida from South America about the first of April. It is not until mid-May, however, that they reach the Great Lakes, New England, and southern Canada. Almost all the other spring migrants arrive before the nighthawk.

At one time the common nighthawk was a bird of the sandy barrens, rocky outcroppings in the mountains, and burned-over land where fires had swept through the trees and scorched the earth. It still favors such places. There, on some bare piece of ground, bald spot, or rocky ledge, it lays its two eggs that are smoke-colored and blend perfectly with their surroundings.

When our industrial cities were built, peaked roofs gave way to flat ones, with a surface of tar and pebbles. This created new nesting possibilities and many nighthawks moved into the cities. Nighthawks are adaptable birds and they are thriving because they are free of most of their natural enemies. Ground animals can no longer raid their nests. The only real hazard is the summer sun that sometimes sends the temperature on the roof up to 130° F. or even 140° F. and melts the tar. Eggs get stuck to the oozing tar, and the young are sometimes scorched to death. Somehow the adults seem to be able to stand the terrific ovenlike heat, and as long as they are not frightened away from their young, they can brood and shade them.

After 19 days the eggs hatch into little

Common nighthawks prefer areas where bare ground is available but have also adapted to city life where they live on the flat roofs of buildings

Common nighthawk

chicks. Their large eyes are open from the first day, and even when they are closed in sleep the youngsters look strangely awake. This is because the large nostrils at the base of the bill look something like a second pair of eyes. They are not naked as young robins are, but are protected by a fuzzy gray down.

Adult nighthawks have very short legs, which they seldom use, so it is unexpected to find that the young can stand upright the very first day out of the egg. They can run with surprising speed across the roof. At three weeks they can make short flights, and at the age of a month they begin to catch moths and other insects.

Nighthawks or bullbats as some people call them, are entirely insectivorous. They have tiny bills, but their huge cavernous mouths can sweep up any flying insect from a mosquito to a large moth. Flying ants often make up a large part of the nighthawk's food; 2,175 of these insects were found in the stomach of one bird. Five hundred mosquitoes were found in another.

By mid-August nighthawks begin to flock. Groups of a dozen to a hundred cruise the open meadows, but there is no diving, no booming, not even the familiar *peent*. They are silent, preparing for the long flight to the South American forests and pampas. By late September they are no longer seen in the North and by mid-October, all but the last few have left the southern United States.

In the low southwestern deserts, the lesser nighthawk, *Chordeiles acutipennis,* is resident. It is smaller and browner than the common nighthawk, with the white patch closer to the tip of the wing. The most outstanding difference is that it flies, as a rule, very low over the ground, never high like the common nighthawk. Its calls are different; often at dusk the desert air is filled with odd clucking and trilling notes from the throats of scores of these birds. In parts of the Southwest both nighthawks are resident; the lesser nighthawk on the low deserts and in the irrigated valleys; the common nighthawk in the mountains, above the pine belt.   —A.B., Jr.

NIGHTSHADE
Black Nightshade
Other Common Names—Deadly nightshade
Scientific Name— *Solanum nigrum*
Family—Solanaceae (nightshade family)
Range—Nova Scotia to Florida and locally westward (introduced from Europe)
Habitat—Waste places, roadsides, and other disturbed soil (seabeaches, etc.)
Time of Blooming—May to October

This plant belongs to the nightshade family which has 1,400 or more members. It is a vine with branches up to 2½ feet long. The white, five-lobed flow-

The deadly nightshade is a relative of such common plants as potato, eggplant, and tobacco

ers are less than half an inch across and are especially sought by bumblebees. As with other flowers of this family the petals of the flower turn backward while the stamens and pistil protrude forward. When ripe the berries are black and hang in loose clusters from slender stems. In some varieties of this species the berries may be poisonous.

Strange as it may seem, this black nightshade is one of the most common plants on some of the outer islands off the Maine coast where the double-crested cormorants and gulls nest. On these islands it grows to an abnormal size due to the guano that is deposited by the birds. The climbing nightshade, *Solanum dulcamara*, which is also a common wild vine of the eastern states, has purple flowers and bright red fruits.

The berries of several species of nightshade in the United States provide food for a long list of wildlife—especially birds. *Solanum dulcamara* is on the protected-flower lists of some states, important not only for the plant itself but also for the creatures that use it for food, and inadvertently transport its seeds in their alimentary tracts to other areas, sometimes miles distant.

The nightshade family contains such well-known food, condiment, and narcotic plants as, potato, tomato, eggplant, cayenne pepper, tobacco, and belladonna.

NUT (*See under Tree: Some North American Nut-bearing Trees*)

Clarke's nutcracker has a short, stout bill with which it can crack a nut in a few well-aimed blows

NUTCRACKER
Clarke's Nutcracker
Other Common Names—Camp robber, meatbird, Clarke's crow
Scientific Name—*Nucifraga columbiana*
Family—Corvidae (jays, magpies, and crows)
Order—Passeriformes
Size—Length, 12½ inches
Range—Central British Columbia, southwestern Alberta, western and central Montana, western and northeastern Wyoming. South through the mountains of Oregon, Washington, central and eastern California to Baja California. South in the Rocky Mountains to eastern Arizona and western New Mexico. Occasionally to central Alaska and east to southern Manitoba, Puget Sound, the Columbia River, southwestern California and southern Arizona. Also southwestern South Dakota, western Nebraska, Kansas, and southwestern Texas

The Clarke's nutcracker inhabits coniferous forests and feeds during the winter primarily on the seeds of spruces, firs, and pines. The cones of these trees are usually loosened by the nutcracker's feet as it swoops down upon a cone-laden branch. Then the bird carries the cone off to a suitable place and knocks off the scales with its bill. In the warmer months, Clarke's nutcrackers feed on a variety of insects—butterfly larvae, beetles, grasshoppers, and crickets—and on berries and flower seeds. The young are fed on hulled pine seeds.

The common names of meatbird and camp robber are often given to this bird because of its habit of eating scraps from picnic tables and refuse around camping areas and lodges. They are especially fond of meat and often sit chattering noisily in the trees around picnickers, waiting for an offering or a chance to raid an unguarded table.

The Clarke's nutcracker was first sighted by Captain William Clarke near Salmon City, Idaho, on August 22, 1805. It is similar to a crow in size and is a drab gray, lighter on the head and almost black on the upper tail coverts. The under tail coverts are white and the wings black, as are the two middle tail feathers.

The nest is usually on pine branches 8 to 40 feet high and is constructed of coarse sticks and twigs on which is placed a smaller nest of grasses, mosses, and strips of juniper bark. Three to five eggs, finely speckled with brown and purple, are laid.   —G.A.B.

NUTHATCH

The nuthatches are small birds with straight, chisel-like bills nearly as long as their heads, long pointed wings and tails that are relatively short and rounded at the tips. They are usually brownish-gray or bluish-gray above and light brown, buff, or white on their underparts. Nuthatches feed chiefly on larvae and insects that they extract from the crevices in tree bark with their strong bills.

The nuthatches are the only members of the family Sittidae and are closely related to the creepers and the titmice; however, unlike these birds they are excellent climbers. They are frequently called upside-down birds because of their ability to walk head down along tree trunks, cliffs, and even stone walls.

These birds are technically grouped with the songbirds because they possess vocal organs. They are not, however, real singers.

Most of the more than 40 species and subspecies of nuthatches are confined to the Old World, and only 4 are residents of North America.

The white-breasted nuthatch, *Sitta carolinensis*, is probably the best known of the North American nuthatches. It is frequently seen among shade trees and in orchards. Its blue-gray back, white cheeks and black cap make it look somewhat like the chickadee.

Smaller than the white-breasted nuthatch, with a broad black line through the eye, the red-breasted nuthatch, *Sitta canadensis*, is a little bird with notes like a tiny horn. Its nest, usually located in the trunk of an evergreen or the scarred and split top of some old tree in the forest, can be recognized by a gummy ring of resin or pitch smeared around the entrance hole.

In the open pine woods of the southeastern United States, there is another species, the brown-headed nuthatch, *Sitta pusilla*, that is even smaller than the red-breasted nuthatch. It has a cinnamon-brown cap, and a conspicuous white spot on the back of the neck. These little birds sometimes go around in large groups, carrying on an excited twittering and chipping while feeding.

The smallest of the whole family is the pigmy nuthatch, *Sitta pygmaea*, that lives in the yellow pine forest of the western states. It is almost identical to the brown-headed nuthatch, both in appearance and actions.

White-breasted nuthatches from Audubon's Elephant Folio

Red-breasted Nuthatch
Other Common Names—Red-bellied nuthatch, Canada nuthatch
Scientific Name—*Sitta canadensis*
Family—Sittidae (nuthatches)
Order—Passeriformes
Size—Length, 4½ to 5 inches
Range—Southeastern Alaska and various parts of Canada south in Appalachians to North Carolina. Also, Michigan, Colorado, and southern California. Sometimes winters as far south as Gulf Coast, Florida, and northern Mexico

The red-breasted nuthatch is a much more unaccountable bird than its relatives, for it comes south in large numbers some winters but not others. Three or four years will pass without any appreciable migration, and then this little bird seems to be everywhere. Possibly such a migration marks a period of large numbers. In such years these little fellows fly past, one by one, on mountain ridges and have been seen crossing large bodies of water, flying in a generally southerly direction. One fall, when the flight was especially heavy, four of them came aboard a codfish boat 10 miles off Cape Cod.

Habits of the Red-breasted Nuthatch
When the time comes for a pair of red-breasted nuthatches to make its nest in the coniferous forest of our Northland, the birds usually dig out a nest chamber in a dead stub, as do the chickadees and woodpeckers. Then the nuthatches line the bottom of the nest cavity with some soft plant material, just as chickadees do. This makes a nest proper for the nuthatch's spotted eggs but is quite different from the way of the woodpeckers, which lay their white eggs on the wooden floor of the nest chamber.

The red-breasted nuthatches' nesting arrangements are not completed, however, until, as a final touch, they bring little globules of pitch, from spruce, pine, or balsam in the tips of their bills, and tap or smear it on the face of the stub about the nest hole. When the nest is new there is less pitch decoration than later, for the birds keep adding to it while raising a family, and may still bring pitch when the young are well-grown in the nest. Even when red-breasted nuthatches nest in a birdhouse, as they have been known to do, they decorate the entrance with pitch. As A. C. Bent wrote in his *Life Histories of North American Nuthatches, Wrens, Thrashers, and Their Allies*, "It is an apparently invariable habit . . ."

Our pioneer ornithologists, Alexander Wilson and John James Audubon, seemed to have missed recording this habit, probably because the breeding range of the red-breasted nuthatch was farther north than the usual range of their field work. The habit has been well known at least since Manly Hardy, of Maine, described it in 1878, in the third volume of the *Bulletin* of the Nuttall Ornithological Club, the publication that six years later became *The Auk*, official publication of the American Ornithologists' Union. Hardy wrote of a nest that had a layer of pitch ¼-inch thick for 2 inches below the nest entrance, the layer then thinned and extended as gummy drops for 21 inches; the pitch layer also extended for 1 inch each side of the opening and 3 inches above it, and many red feathers from the underparts of the birds were stuck in the pitch.

Hardy wrote that the pitch was for the protection of the nest, but did not say against what. Many later naturalists have observed this habit and speculated in vain as to its use. The best theory they could come up with was that it kept ants from getting into the nest, or that some of the drops of pitch resembled eyes and so frightened away predators. This last is the same sort of idea that has been advanced as a reason for the snake skins in the nests of great crested flycatchers—that they frighten away predators.

It has even been suggested that this pitch decoration is a drawback to the birds, for they get feathers stuck in it, and pitch stuck on their feathers causes excessive wear on those of the underparts. An inspection of two trays of specimens of red-breasted nuthatches in the Chicago Natural History Museum revealed that they were markedly worn and ragged, especially some of the summer specimens. Some of them had little black spots of pitch stuck in their feathers.

As long as naturalists were looking for advantages to the bird in this pitch-plastering, they could not improve on the comment of E.H. Forbush in his monumental *Birds of Massachusetts and Other New England States,* in which he wrote: "The origin of this habit and its possible utility has never been explained satisfactorily."

There is another way of looking at bird habits that will help in understanding the present case. It is necessary to use it in understanding how it is that the downy woodpecker lays white eggs on the bare wood floor of its nest cavity and hatches young devoid of down, in the same woodlot where the chickadees and nuthatches, which also dig out nest chambers in stubs, build a *nest* in the cavity, lay *spotted* eggs, and hatch out young bearing tufts of down. Presumably the woodpecker's way is the more efficient. It is simpler, and presumably chickadees and nuthatches could get along just as well if they did not go to the trouble of lining their nest cavities, and without the extra tax on their metabolism of producing color for the eggs, and that of their young in growing down.

By looking at the other members of the large woodpecker family, Picidae, of more than 200 species (also some of the related families such as those of honey guides, barbets, and toucans of the tropics), one finds that hole nesting is the usual condition with them. The nest cavity is not lined, nor are the eggs

pigmented, nor do the newly hatched young have down. Perhaps these are ancient adaptations to hole nesting in the interests of economy, and are old in the group. In any case, the downy woodpecker is simply following in the tradition of its relatives and is not adapting its nest habits to the conditions in the forest that we know.

The nuthatches and the chickadees belong to the great assemblage of birds called songbirds, the suborder Oscines, which includes so many of our common garden birds. Most of them build nests in the open, lay colored eggs, and their young are downy. Only here and there have they broken with tradition, nesting in holes like bank swallows and house wrens; laying white eggs, like the dipper and short-billed marsh wren; or having naked newly hatched young, like blue jays and cedar waxwings. The chickadees and nuthatches have broken with tradition in nesting in holes, but they still conform with most of their close relatives in building a nest, in laying colored eggs (usually), and in their young having natal down. Presumably their ancestors in the not-too-distant past nested in the open, and the habit of the present-day birds still accords with that of their relatives.

These points of difference in the breeding biology of the red-breasted nuthatch and the downy woodpecker may show the woodpecker as a better-adapted hole nester: the better-adjusted bird. The differences, however, are understandably not in relation to the environment, but in the light of the different history and heredity of the two birds as is seen by examining their relatives.

One should consider the habit of pitch decorating of the red-breasted nuthatch by using the same approach. What do its relatives do? The nuthatches are usually grouped with or near the various creepers, wall creepers, titmice, and Australian and Madagascar nuthatches, and there is considerable diversity of opinion as to where to draw the family lines, as well as an uncomfortable feeling that this assemblage may be merely an ecological grouping of creeping, climbing bird acrobats.

Be that as it may, the typical nuthatches of some 16 species are much alike in general habits and appearance, and if one knows one species he would recognize any of them as nuthatches, if he allowed for a variation in habits of some of the Asiatic species in climbing on rocks as well as on trees.

The other three species that live in America — the white-breasted nuthatch (which nests in natural cavities) and the pigmy and brown-headed nuthatches, which dig their own nest holes, help us little though we note that the white-breasted nuthatch has been known to carry in earth or mud and put it on the floor of its nest, and the pigmy nuthatch is said to calk and weather-strip its nest cavity.

In the Old World the rest of the 16 species of nuthatches live with their headquarters in the Himalayan region. In the comparatively small country of Burma there are six species, though but one reaches western Europe and only two reach the islands of the Malay Archipelago. They are absent from the African and the Australian region, as they are from South America.

All the Eurasian species nest in holes, but there is a wide variation in just how they do it. The North American red-breasted nuthatch reappears in two far separated localities, on Corsica and in North China, and simply digs a hole in a rotten stub. The vividly blue-backed, velvet-fronted nuthatch that ranges into the tropics of the Indies uses natural cavities but often enlarges them and sometimes improves them by plastering the walls or entrance with mud. The European nuthatch, which ranges from southern Asia to western Europe, uses natural cavities and calks the cracks with mud, and reduces the size of the entrance hole with masonry of mud, until only an opening of the proper size is left. The most unusual of all, the rock nuthatch, which ranges westward only as far as southern Europe, selects a natural hole in a tree, among rocks, or in a rock and mud wall and may line it completely with mud and continue the mud lining as an entrance tube as much as 6 to 10 inches long. This masonry becomes very hard. In addition, the rock nuthatch is said to attach feathers on the face of the rock or tree around the nest opening. All the species apparently make a nest proper within the nest cavity.

From these data we can arrange a series from simple nesting in natural cavities (white-breasted nuthatch); modifying natural cavities by enlarging them and sometimes using a plaster of mud (velvet-fronted nuthatch); from here the series branches two ways: One culminates in complete excavating of a nest with a little plastering of pitch about the entrance (red-breasted) and a simple excavation by the brown-headed nuthatch. The nesting habits of other nuthatches vary from a calking of cracks

Red-breasted nuthatch

Brown-headed nuthatch

Pigmy nuthatch

A red-breasted nuthatch feeds its young on a lichen-covered limb

and a reducing of the size of the entrance with mud plaster, to the elaborate plastering of the rock nuthatch.

The red-breasted nuthatch is seen to have developed its nesting habits along the lines of being independent of natural cavities by digging its own nest hole, but has carried along one of the traits of its relatives: the plastering about the entrance to its nest, even though this plastering serves no useful purpose. The nest lining in the cavity, the color of the eggs, and the down on the young also could be dispensed with. Perhaps the occasional mud in the nest of the white-breasted nuthatch and the calking and weather-stripping of the pigmy nuthatch are similar examples of ancient behavior patterns that still persist.

By looking at the plastering habits of the red-breasted nuthatch against the background of the habits of its relatives, one can understand how it came about. The habit is a relic, a hangover from the days when it was part of a functional process. It is a relic just as the buttons on a man's coat sleeve and the button-hole on his left lapel are nonessential now, though once the buttons on the cuff had buttonholes to match, and the buttonhole on the lapel, which now may hold a flower, once had a button to help the coat protect the man's throat.

These statements are figures of speech, shortcuts to the elaborate, guarded phrases in which the precision of the scientist expresses matters of evolution, descent with modification, and inheritance of characters. The only justification for using them is to make the matter more clear. —A.L.R.

White-breasted Nuthatch
Other Common Names—Common nuthatch, devil downhead
Scientific Name—*Sitta carolinensis*
Family—Sittidae (nuthatches)
Order—Passeriformes
Size—Length, five to six inches
Range—Southern Canada, northern Montana, Maine, central Nova Scotia south to Gulf Coast, Florida, Baja California, and Mexico. Absent in the Great Plains area of the United States

White-breasted nuthatches are stockily built, broad through the shoulders, and stubby-tailed. They do not use their tails as props the way the woodpeckers and creepers do, but just clamber over the rough branches in awkward, jerky hitches. It often follows chickadees and titmice through the woodlands and orchards; however, it is easy to distinguish the nuthatch by its call—a nasal *yank*. Late in winter, on days when there is a touch of spring in the air, the nuthatch is spurred on to more elaborate vocal efforts. The song is a hurried nasal series of notes, all on the same pitch, something like *hah-hah-hah-hah-hah-hah-hah*.

Although the white-breasted nuthatch is just a little bird, it can look twice its size by spreading its wings and tail to their fullest extent, revealing a remarkable pattern of gray, black, and white. This fluffing out not only seems to impress its mate but is sometimes used to drive other birds away, especially sparrows and chickadees at the feeding tray.

An old downy woodpecker hole makes a perfect nesting site. Any knothole or natural cavity, with a properly sized opening will do, and nuthatches will also nest in man-made birdhouses. If necessary, the nuthatches can excavate homes for themselves. The bottom of the hole is filled with fine strips of bark and lined with soft hair, fur, or moss. Nest building keeps the birds busy for several days, the male passing the materials through the hole, the female arranging them inside.

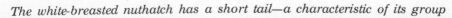

The white-breasted nuthatch has a short tail—a characteristic of its group

White-breasted nuthatch families are large; seldom less than 6 eggs are laid—usually there are 8, or even 10 or 11. Instead of bringing up two broods of four each, as so many other birds do, the nuthatch raises one large brood a year. After 10 or 12 days of incubation, the eggs hatch into blind and naked young. When they feather out and leave the cramped quarters of the dark hole, they look very much like the adults—gray back, white cheeks, and black cap, but for two weeks or more they must be fed until they learn how to find food for themselves.

The strong bill, which acts like a chisel, can pry into crevices in the bark where insect larvae or egg masses are hidden. Scale insects, weevils, leaf beetles, click beetles, plant lice, and many other insects are eaten. The stomach of one white-breasted nuthatch that was examined contained 1,629 eggs of the fall cankerworm.

Except in the summer when the families are still together, white-breasted nuthatches seldom gather in flocks of a dozen or more the way chickadees often do. Usually there is but a pair of birds accompanying the winter flock of chickadees; three or four at most, but in the vicinity of the feeding tray, sometimes half a dozen nuthatches will gather. Suet is a favorite food, but the big sunflower seeds, which the chickadees and blue jays prefer, are also eaten by the nuthatches. They take the seeds, one at a time, and wedge them tightly in a crack in the bark, then with swift blows of the chisel-like bill, split them open to get at the kernel inside. Nuthatches open acorns and small nuts the same way, which has undoubtedly given them the name of *nuthatch*.

Recommended Reading

Life Histories of North American Nuthatches, Wrens, Thrashers, and Allies—A. C. Bent. U.S. Government Printing Office, Washington, D.C. **Stray Feathers from a Bird Man's Desk**—Austin L. Rand. Doubleday & Company, Garden City, New York.

OAK

The oaks are a large group of trees that have a wide distribution, particularly in North America and Europe. More than 300 species are known. Of this number, some 44 to 85 species are native to North America north of Mexico. These plants are closely related to the beeches, chestnuts, and chinquapins and are classified with them in the family Fagaceae (*See also Beech; and Chestnut*).

The Fagaceae are characterized by the distinctive catkins of the male flowers, and the single or paired female flowers, completely lacking in petals, that grow in the axils of the leaves. The oaks (*Quercus*) are easily separated from the other trees in the beech family by the *acorns* that are produced as mature fruits. Only the genus *Quercus* (oaks) and the genus *Lithocarpus* (tanbark oak) bear these cupped nutlets.

The various species of oaks are usually divided into two groups; those in each group look somewhat alike and therefore seem to be more closely related than to other oaks. In the *white oak group*, the winter buds are blunt (except in the chestnut oak), the leaf lobes are rounded without bristled tips, the acorns ripen in one year, and the bark is usually light colored. This group includes the following familiar species:

White oak—*Quercus alba*
Post oak—*Quercus stellata*
Bur oak—*Quercus macrocarpa*

The white oak attains impressive dimensions and may live 800 or more years

Swamp white oak—*Quercus bicolor*
Chestnut oak—*Quercus muehlenbergii*
Live oak—*Quercus virginiana*
Valley oak—*Quercus lobata*
Oregon white oak—*Quercus garryana*
Gambel oak—*Quercus gambelli*

The *black oak group* has sharp-pointed winter buds, more or less pointed leaf lobes with bristle tips, acorns that ripen in two years, and bark that is usually dark colored. Representative species in the black oak group are:

Black oak—*Quercus velutina*
Pin oak—*Quercus palustris*
Scarlet oak—*Quercus coccinea*
Red oak—*Quercus rubra*
Jack oak—*Quercus ellipsoidalis*
Spanish oak—*Quercus falcata*
Scrub oak—*Quercus ilicifolia*
Blackjack oak—*Quercus marilandica*
Water oak—*Quercus nigra*
Laurel-leafed oak—*Quercus laurifolia*
Turkey oak—*Quercus incana*

Willow oak—*Quercus phellos*
California black oak—*Quercus kelloggi*

Oaks are perhaps the most important of all trees as a source of food for mammals and birds because of the abundance of the fruits or acorns they produce and the large numbers of these trees especially in eastern forests. On the Pacific Coast, 10 species of oak grow in mountain valleys, humid coastal forests, or arid interior regions. The western plains have 9 species, and the eastern forests, 36 species. Only in the north central plains are the oaks poorly represented; one species grows there as a native tree.

The small acorns of water oak, pin oak, and willow oak are eaten by quail and ducks. Wild turkeys feed on acorns of all sizes. The stomach of one wild turkey was found to contain 77 black oak acorns.

Many mammals, including bears, beavers, hares, muskrats, opossums, rabbits, raccoons, squirrels, and deer feed on oak acorns. In Texas 52 percent of the white-tailed deer's diet is supplied by the twigs, foliage, and acorns of oaks.

Among the smaller mammals, many species feed on acorns. Chipmunks, pocket gophers, ground squirrels, rats, and mice are fond of them. Many of these mammals store the acorns for winter feeding.

Birds such as chickadees, goldfinches, crows, grackles, jays, meadowlarks, thrushes, woodpeckers, and wrens eat the sweet nutlets.   —G.A.B.

Black Oak

Other Common Names — Yellow oak, yellow-bark oak, quercitron oak
Scientific Name — *Quercus velutina*
Family — Fagaceae (beech family)
Range — Central New England, west to southeastern Minnesota, and south to eastern Texas and northern Florida (absent from southern Coastal Plain)
Habitat — Needs sun and grows on rather open, gently sloping hillsides and flatlands, sometimes in quite gravelly soils if enough subsurface water is present

Leaves — Bristle-tipped as in all the black oaks, shiny above, with a squarish overall outline. Yellowish fuzz where veins and midrib meet on the underside, sometimes over the whole undersurface of the leaf. Depth and shape of the spaces between the lobes is highly variable, some of the leaves resembling those of pin, scarlet, or blackjack oaks. Length, 4 to 12 inches
Bark — Rather smooth, shiny olive-gray on young trees and smaller branches, soon splitting to become rough, dark and gravelly. Trunks of older trees show a rather uniform pattern of vertical cracks and crosschecking, with bark usually gray-brown or blackish-brown, although sometimes light gray. Underbark yellow
Flower — Male blossoms are four- to six-inch catkins that appear with the opening leaves, usually in May. Female

Black oak

blossoms are inconspicuous
Fruit — A rather short, light-colored acorn, one-half to three-fourths of an inch across, set in a rough, scaly cup. Ripening in the second year

Because of the variety in the shape of its leaves the black oak is not always easy to identify with certainty at first, but once the character of the rather stiff, glossy foliage, the bark, and the typical overall shape of the tree becomes familiar, it can be recognized at a glance, even at some distance.

In wilder, forested country young black oaks tend to grow in open locations, for considerable sunlight is necessary for them to flourish. Roadsides, margins of farms, and flatlands along railroad tracks are also favorite locations. The trees are frequently seen on private lawns in suburban areas. In such locations the dark bark and rugged but irregular form of the well-trimmed larger trees are quite distinctive. Squirrels often make their nests high up in such trees and feed upon the bitter acorns that are produced in large crops during some years, very sparsely in others.

The coarse-grained hard wood is considered inferior to white oak for most purposes but is used for construction, flooring, inexpensive furniture, and fuel. A very large black oak may measure 120 feet or more in height with a trunk 5 feet through, although more usual dimensions are 80 feet high by 3 or 4 feet in diameter.

When growing in poor, sandy, or gravelly soils and subjected to much hot weather or burned back by fires, black oak sprouts; and coppice growth may bear broad, tough leaves that much resemble the blackjack oak, *Quercus marilandica,* generally a small, scrubby tree. This appears often to be the case with the black oak group where they have had to adapt to severe soil and weather conditions. To further complicate matters, at least four black oak hybrids are recognized — the result of natural crossbreeding with other species of the group.   —M.H.B.

Bur Oak
Other Common Names—Mossy cup oak
Scientific Name—*Quercus macrocarpa*
Family—Fagaceae (beech family)
Range — Southern New Brunswick to southeastern Manitoba, and Maine to southeastern Montana; south to Virginia (away from coastal plain and piedmont) and central Texas
Habitat—Typically a bottomlands species in rich woods and on fertile slopes
Leaves—6 to 12 inches long and round-lobed; with one pair of deeply cut sinuses

Bur oak (above); post oak (below)

near the middle. Paler below
Bark—Darker gray than white oak, with a brownish cast and more sharply ridged. Rough and loose on branches; the twigs may have corky wings like sweet gum
Flowers—Typical oak catkins, male five to six inches long
Fruit—Acorns of variable shape and size (three-fourths to two inches long) but always deeply set in a rough cup that has a bristly or curly fringe around the edge

The bur oak is one of the largest of the North American oaks, attaining heights of up to 180 feet with a trunk 7 feet in diameter. It is often called the mossy cup oak because of the heavy fringe on the acorn cups. In the Mississippi Valley these cups are so large that they are referred to as "bird nest cups."

The twigs of bur oaks are a sure means of identification because of the development of corky projections that are often present and stand out on each side of the twigs up to 1½ inches. Few trees have these corky wings (*See under Gum*).

Bur oaks are frequently planted along streets where they develop a pleasing form. They are resistant to smoke and insect enemies and grow rapidly.

—G.A.B.

Live oak

Live Oak
Other Common Names—None
Scientific Name—*Quercus virginiana*
Family—Fagaceae (beech family)
Range—Mostly coastal, from extreme southeastern Virginia through Florida and along Gulf Coast to west central Texas and northern Mexico
Habitat—Sandy, dry or wet soil and coastal sandhills and dunes
Leaves—Two to five inches long and about half as wide, stiff, glossy dark-green above with curved-down edges; paler (sometimes brownish) and fuzzy on the underside. They last through the winter but are shed when the new ones appear. Occasionally with wavy, shallow-lobed margins
Bark—A quite dark gray-brown surface, cracked and grooved, sometimes almost black when damp. May be covered with pale lichens as well as being draped with graceful festoons of Spanish moss
Flower—Male: small, yellow oak catkins about two to three inches long. Female: in small spikes on stems, about the same length
Fruit—Small, slim, inverted oval acorns, growing singly or in groups, set in shallow cups

Along with the southern pines, cypress, and magnolia, the live oak is very typically a tree of the American south, especially of the lower coastal plain where it attains impressive size and form. Although never very tall (60 feet is near the maximum) the heavy branches usually arch away from the very short base and then sweep over and down and up at the ends, almost touching the ground and making the total width of the tree as much as three times its height. The bulk of the foliage is on the outer ends of the branches, emphasizing the broad, rounded crown and producing under it a cavernous shelter, usually heavily draped with Spanish moss.

The dignity and expanse of such trees have impressed many people and, as with the American elm, there are groups who make a hobby of locating giant live oaks, measuring them, calculating their probable age and trying to assure their preservation (*See also Elm*).

Probably these trees have enjoyed a large measure of informal protection since early plantation days, but in addition they were also cut for shipbuilding and other purposes. The very heavy, dense wood, which is considered unsurpassed for such work, was often especially cut to take advantage of the turn of a trunk or branch in making curved structural members for a ship's keel or hull. Pieces with a continuous grain that had virtually no weakness were obtained in this way. So important was this use of live oak when the nation's merchant and naval vessels were built of wood that Congress arranged to acquire live oak forests for the government.

The very small, leathery leaves of this tree seem to tolerate the effects of hot, sandy country and ocean weather remarkably well, and it is often the first species of tree encountered behind the beach dunes. Many birds, mammals, and air plants (*see Epiphyte*) regularly find lodging in live oaks and feed upon the acorns.   — M.H.B.

Pin Oak
Other Common Names — Swamp oak, swamp Spanish oak
Scientific Name — *Quercus palustris*
Family — Fagaceae (beech family)
Range — Rhode Island and central Massachusetts, west to southern Michigan and southeastern Nebraska; south to eastern Oklahoma, and central North Carolina, except for high Appalachians
Habitat — A swamp species, particularly abundant in woods with clayey soils subject to frequent flooding, although it will grow under different conditions
Leaves — Smaller than those of most oaks (four to six inches long) but bristle-tipped like the other members of the black oak group. Leaves on older trees

Pin oak

are dark green with a few narrow lobes and wide interspaces. On young and seedling trees, paler green and more elongate with more filled-in lobes
Bark — Smooth on young trees and upper trunks, somewhat spotted and speckled with twig scars. Some smoothness retained to a considerable age
Flower — Catkins smaller and thinner than those of the black oak but appearing about the same time in spring. Female blossoms inconspicuous
Fruit — Short, buttonlike acorns in shallow cups barely half an inch across, often in clusters

Although the pin oak is fond of water and is apt to grow in swamp and lowland areas subject to frequent flooding, it also grows on slopes, in thickets, and has been planted with outstanding success on private grounds and along parkways. A particularly representative growth of pin oak forms in wet flatwoods bordering level pasture areas.

Many people, upon first seeing a pin oak think the tree is diseased or in poor condition because of the abundance of dead lower branches that remain on the trunk. This is merely a characteristic of pin oaks and may be seen on the largest healthiest trees. Other particularly helpful identification marks are the small, deeply cut leaves, that give the foliage a perforated appearance, and the little, round acorns.

Squirrels and various birds including some hawks nest in these trees and the acorn mast that accumulates under them offers a reliable food source to many nut-eaters including mice, ground-feeding birds, jays, and certain ducks. The latter find easy access to many of these trees because they so often grow near water. Generally no great quantity of pin oak is lumbered except as part of a general cutting, for the wood is apt to be knotty; but it is encouraged as a woodlot tree and is used for fuel. —M.H.B.

Post Oak
Other Common Names—None
Scientific Name—*Quercus stellata*
Family—Fagaceae (beech family)
Range—Long Island, New York, west to southeastern Nebraska and south to the Gulf Coast
Habitat—Dry soils
Leaves—Distinctive, cross-shaped leaves, the two middle lobes being squarish and opposite, with dense yellow fuzz below
Bark—Gray-brown, fissured, and somewhat flaky
Flower—Typical oak catkins
Fruit—Small acorns one-half inch long. Cup less warty than in other white oaks

Post oak often grows in company with southern pine and willow oak, but in the more prairielike country west of the Mississippi the tree grows in scattered fashion or in small forest areas, often with an undergrowth of prickly pear cactus. Its foliage is rather thick, though, fuzzy, and shiny; the branches and trunk are apt to be stout and gnarled; and the crown of the tree, low and rounded. In prairie areas it shows itself to be a species rather well adapted to dry or sandy conditions, but in regions where the soil is richer and water is more abundant it looks more like the other eastern oaks and may grow to 90 or 100 feet in height. The bark, which looks somewhat like that of a young black oak that has been grown in rather poor, dry soils, is split and cracked into narrow ridges and blocks.

Post oak lumber is very hard, heavy and durable, and is used for railroad ties, fence posts, and fuel. Like many oaks with tough leaves its foliage stays on rather late in the year, turning to yellow and brown.   —M.H.B.

Northern Red Oak
Other Common Names—Red oak
Scientific Name—*Quercus rubra borealis*
Family—Fagaceae (beech family)
Range—Nova Scotia, southern Quebec, Ontario, and Maine to Minnesota; south to northeastern Oklahoma, and to the piedmont of the southern states
Habitat—The predominant forest tree in many northeastern areas, especially dry upland woods
Leaves—Six to nine inches long with bristle-tipped lobes. General outline, oval; widest about the middle. Bristles hairlike, lobes pointed but not deep (usually four or more on each side). Not shiny; no yellowish fuzz below
Bark—Smooth and rather light gray when young, splitting with age to form noticeable stripes, or elongate, diamond-shaped ridges of rough, dark brown. Very large trees show a broken network of the lighter tones on a hard, grooved or wrinkled surface of darker gray or brown
Flower—The male catkins, three to five inches long and appearing in May or June, look much like those of the black oak but are a little smaller
Fruit—A plump-looking acorn often a full inch long, rather straight-sided with a distinctive shallow cup. Trees with

more pointed acorns and deeper cups may be hybrids

Many oaks turn red in the autumn including young pin and black oaks, scarlet. oak, and others. Northern red oak is generally a more common tree than any of these and in some highland areas around the Appalachian Mountains it predominates over all other species of trees. It may be that this condition was brought about in part by the virtual extinction of American chestnut by an introduced fungus blight (*See Chestnut*). The opening up of the forest as the American chestnut died off, left space in many eastern forests that was quickly occupied by the red oak.

In the woods one of the chief identification marks of red oak is the tendency of the smoother young bark to split into longitudinal ridges—a feature usually most noticeable part way up the rather tall trunk. These trees are frequently 80 to 100 feet high with trunks 2 to 3 feet in diameter but when grown in open areas in rich pastureland or on estate grounds, red oak may reach an even greater height and develop a very broad crown supported by a trunk up to 5 or even 6 feet in diameter that usually flairs out to a massive base. The robust form combined with the hard bark suggest, quite accurately, a tree of great toughness, strength, and vitality. Further, red oak is generally one of the faster growing species of its group and provides a good and fairly frequent harvest when it is commercially grown for lumber. Construction timbers, railroad ties and strong, heavy furniture are common uses for its heavy, strong, grainy wood.

From a distance red oak can often be recognized during the summer months by the way its leaves grow in clumps at the ends of the branches, arching outwards and down from the twig in somewhat loose, palmate fashion quite different from the springy, irregular leaf

Red oak

positions on the black oak. In addition, red oak leaves are rather deep bluish-green and never really shiny. If acorns are present, these are immediately recognizable by their shallow cups and large stout form, the largest of any of the members of the black oak group. Generally it makes an excellent shade tree if one is looking for a durable species and fairly quick results. Of particular help in getting a nice tree and rapid growth is avoiding injury to the main terminal bud or stem when it is young.
                                    —M.H.B.

Oregon white oak (right) ; valley oak (left)

Valley Oak
Other Common Names — California white oak, rable
Scientific Name — *Quercus lobata*
Family — Fagaceae (beech family)
Range — The Sacramento-San Joaquin Valley of California, west into the Coast Ranges and south to about Los Angeles
Habitat — A tree of hot interior lands, where it grows in open groves
Leaves — Two to four inches long, leathery and many-lobed with fuzzy hairs on both sides
Bark — Pale gray; on older trees, thick, deeply cracked and cross-checked, looking like alligator leather
Flower — Two- to three-inch, yellow, male catkins in early spring; female flowers inconspicuous
Fruit — Surprisingly large, elongate and pointed acorns, 1¼ to 2½ inches long, set in quite deep, warty cups

The valley oak often reaches great size, with an extraordinarily thick but usually very short trunk and a span sometimes equalling that of the American elm and live oak of the Atlantic seaboard. Although its wood has not been as highly regarded for shipbuilding as the eastern species it has been used for this purpose, but its greatest value and charm is in the living trees that grace many valley areas in California back of the immediate coast. Perhaps because of a warmer climate it grows somewhat faster than many eastern white oaks but is apparently more brittle and more easily damaged by storms. The noticeably long, pointed acorns of a shape characteristic of several West Coast species have, like many other white oaks, a fairly sweet edible nut, or kernel, once eaten by the Indians that lived in the area. These are still used as food for domestic livestock.
— M.H.B.

White Oak
Other Common Names — None
Scientific Name — *Quercus alba*
Family — Fagaceae (beech family)

Range — Southern New Brunswick, southern Quebec, southern Ontario, and Maine to Minnesota, south to eastern Texas and northern Florida
Habitat — Dry woods but tolerant of many conditions
Leaves — Dark green with a faint bluish-white bloom, distinctly paler beneath, with rounded lobes characteristic of the white oak group. The lobes may be deeply cut, almost to the midrib, or only slightly indented on the margin
Bark — Pale gray or spotty gray and brown with big, lengthwise flakes or strips on younger trees and branches. Old trunks have a thicker, tighter bark with a more uniformly grooved and cracked texture
Flower — Rather short (two to three inches) male catkins, often pink-tinted, appearing with the tiny new leaves in midspring
Fruit — An acorn about three-fourths of an inch long whose prominent cup has a granular, beaded surface. Matures during the first year (unlike black oaks), is edible, has a pleasant sweet flavor

Of many species of the white oak group this is generally the most abundant one in the East. It is a fine durable tree, widely known for its good looks, its rugged wood, and characteristic leaf shape so widely used in design and art forms. These are particularly attractive in the spring when the catkins are coming out — little soft pink or red miniatures that hang down in pyramidal groups on the upturned tips of the stems. As with most oaks these details are best seen on small saplings and coppice growths along the roadside and forest margins.

White oaks have often been left by farmers clearing fields. In such situations white oaks may grow to impressive dimensions and considerable age. Trees up to 800 years old are known. Generally, any very large white oak may be considered quite old; for it hardly approaches red oak in its growth rate. According to soil and weather conditions

The acorns of oaks, such as these from a white oak, provide food for a great variety of wild creatures

Blackjack oak is a member of the black oak group

big trees will vary from 70 to as much as 150 feet high with trunks up to 8 feet in diameter. These latter figures certainly represent massive living things equal in their own habitat to the giant conifers of the West. They make excellent street and lawn trees of great strength and beauty, generally very free from disease and so deeply rooted as to be almost impervious to severe wind damage. The chief care that should be taken on planting them is in spacing the trees widely apart.

The name white oak, given because of the pale bark, appears to be used with remarkable consistency in the lumber trade where names seem often to be changed around to describe properties of this or that wood. White oak wood is prized for its solidity and strength, and weighs 48 pounds per cubic foot when properly dried. Bridge and shipbuilding, rugged but good looking furniture, flooring and special cabinet work are among its better uses. Premature or too frequent cutting of white oak or actually any forest is an unwise, shortsighted practice, for most trees grow slowly and require high quality nourishment for high quality results.　　　　　　　　　　—M.H.B.

Oregon White Oak
Other Common Names—Garry oak, Oregon oak
Scientific Name—*Quercus garryona*
Family—Fagaceae (beech family)
Range—Southern British Columbia, western Washington and Oregon, south into western California as far as Monterey Bay
Habitat—Intermountain valleys and lower slopes
Leaves—Four to six inches long, thick and shiny above, yellowish and fuzzy with prominent veins below
Bark—Light gray to warm brown, broken into many squarish plates on the larger trunks
Flower—Clusters of rather hairy oak catkins
Fruit—Fat, round acorns an inch or so long and three-fourths of an inch wide, set in a moderately shallow cup

The Oregon white oak is a large tree with soft deciduous foliage, associated with forested areas and open, natural parklands. In fertile valleys the Oregon white oak attains a size and form equal to many eastern white oaks and has qualities of leaf shape and acorns not too unlike some English oaks. On higher slopes and in poorer soils it is apt to be smaller or even shrublike as with the scrub oaks of our eastern and southwestern states.　　　　　—M.H.B.

OAK WORM (*See under Insect: Insect Control*)

OCEANIC BIRDS (*See under Bird: Birds of the Ocean; and under Hurricane*)

OCEANOGRAPHY (*See under Seashore: Life of the Seashore*)

OCELOT (*See under Cats of North America*)

OCTOPUS

Octopuses are marine animals with eight tentacles surrounding a beaked mouth, two large eyes above a braincase of cartilage, and a rounded, pulpy body. They are mollusks, of the family Octopodidae. Along with the squids and the sea slugs, they have lost the calcareous shell that characterizes the other mollusks; in this group, only two small internal rods of chiton remain of the ancestral exoskeleton (*See Mollusk*).

The highest intelligence and the best developed nervous system of all of the invertebrates are found in the octopus. These creatures can remember and, to some degree, reason. Their eyesight is extremely good, and their emotions are reflected in the changing colors of their skin.

Crabs, clams, and mussels are the chief food of octopuses. The prey is killed by

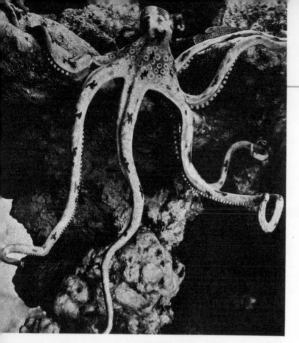

Octopus

venom, then torn apart by the suckers that border the tentacles. The octopus itself is preyed upon by all manner of large fishes; its only defense is flight and the ejection of ink that contains chemicals that may paralyze the sense of smell of the pursuer.

Octopuses hide in crevices, emerging to slither over the bottom, often changing color to match it. They can swim rapidly by jet propulsion, taking a quantity of air into the mantle and expelling it through a siphon; the bulky abdomen precedes the rest of the body, and the tentacles trail along behind.

In mating, the male places the specialized tip of one tentacle, that has been smeared with sperm cells, into the mantle of the female. It is broken off and remains there. The male grows a replacement.

Octopuses are especially common in tropical seas, and are often eaten by natives. They are considered a great delicacy by gourmets. They have also been used to recover pottery jars; when lowered on a rope, the octopus hides in the nearest hole, and if the hole turns out to be a jar, both octopus and jar can be hauled to the surface. In some areas, empty jars are used as octopus traps.

—G.B.S.

OIL POLLUTION
A Brief History of Oil Pollution

Pollution of the sea from waste oil has caused the destruction of thousands of seabirds. It has been going on since the change from coal-burning to oil-burning ships, which can be assigned to the second decade of the 20th Century. Oil-burning and oil-carrying ships, that is tankers, have to discharge their waste oil somewhere. It is extremely tempting to dump it into the sea.

During the early 1920's, various countries passed legislation prohibiting the discharge of waste oil in their territorial waters and thus protected themselves as far as they were able. However, oil will travel enormous distances. It has been proved to travel on the surface of the sea for hundreds of miles. The nations of Europe are connected along a very small seaboard compared with that of the United States. There, only concerted international action could deal with the problem, which is why in 1926 a preliminary governmental conference on the subject was held. It was held in Washington, D.C. As a consequence, a draft convention was drawn up, and the main feature was that each country should establish an area off its shores in which no oil should be discharged.

For administrative convenience, the distance was put at 50 miles, though certain countries were allowed to extend it to 150 miles. All this, unfortunately, was not ratified. All of the very important shipping companies of Great Britain voluntarily observe the 50-mile limit and have gone on doing so ever since. They also voluntarily equipped their ships with separators, in those ships that had not had them before. Oil pollution of the seas continued because there were ships traveling around the east Atlantic, sailing under other flags.

The subject was brought up at the League of Nations in 1934 by the British delegate. It was referred to the Communications and Transit Organization, and the question was studied there. International questionnaires were sent out, and all sorts of questions were asked—in fact, a good deal of paper work took place, but World War II came which ended the investigation. However it was not completely ended because people already had been prompted to do some of the researches and observations on such pressing problems as, how far oil would actually travel; and how far oil travel coincided with surface current travel. There had been a lot of exploration of surface currents, too, all of which has been intensified in the eastern Atlantic.

During the Second World War, Britain was bathed in oil for obvious and often tragic reasons, but people wondered when the war was ended if they would be able to get rid of the problem of oil pollution, once and for all. However, a new fact had been introduced into the business, because in Britain and in other parts of Europe, enormous numbers of oil refineries had been set up. Oil had been previously refined in the country of its origin. Between World War II and 1951, crude oil imported into Britain alone increased seven times.

During the winter of 1951—52, which was a winter of considerable floating oil in the Atlantic Ocean, it was estimated that the number of seabirds observed oiled around the coast of the British Isles was somewhere around 100,000. It is certain that after those 35 years, which is the period in which there has been oiling in Britain, the number of the auks, particularly the guillemots, (called murres in the United States) had seriously decreased, especially around those colonies in areas like the Firth of Clyde, and certain other parts of Scotland which are notoriously bad areas for oil pollution. There is more particularly a small colony of guillemots and puffins on Ailsa Craig in the Firth of Clyde where at the end

Oil slicks on the surface of water are a serious threat to waterfowl

of the century there were certainly tens of thousands of birds there. In the 1950's there were only a few hundreds of each kind, although later, since there was less oil in the Clyde, they began regaining their numbers. However, one cannot be absolutely sure that this decrease was directly correlated with oil, although there had not been a decrease in auks in other parts of Britain, where there was no oil pollution.

In March 1952 there was a serious case of oil pollution on the coast of Gotland in Sweden in the Baltic Sea that caused the deaths of 30,000 seabirds. There were other reports of the destruction of large numbers of birds, by waste oil, from Belgium, Denmark, and Holland at just about the same time. The North Sea at times was very bad. Also there was no doubt that the number of birds that were seen dead as the result of oiling were but a fraction of the total numbers killed. This was especially so when there was oil in fairly open waters where auks were feeding, and a greater number of them went to the bottom before they could be washed ashore.

The oil gets into the interstices of a seabird's feathers and destroys the heat insulation there. Very often, oiled birds die of exposure, or die of starvation because they can not feed quickly enough to keep up their body temperatures. Also, oiled birds are impeded in seeking their prey.

The International Council for Bird Preservation assisted in assembling the facts, and they were in the forefront of signing the resolution to this problem of oil pollution, and to put on international pressure. For years and years the resolution had been passed at international conferences, but nothing practical came of it.

In March 1952, on the initiative of the British section of the International Council for Bird Protection, James Callaghan, a member of the British Parliament, and various interested organizations and individuals, had a meeting at the House of Commons in London to discuss pressing for more active effort to solve the oil pollution problem. Many interests were represented—resorts, fisheries, national wildlife protection societies. All became united on the problem and almost exactly the same thing happened among the Scandinavian countries in the same year.

In 1953 an extremely useful report was published that really triggered an unofficial international conference on oil pollution of the sea, organized in London in October 1953 by the British independent committee. The conference was attended by representatives of 28 countries. It was an interesting example of international enterprise, by societies in which nobody waited for UN or UNESCO or anybody else to come along and do something. They did it themselves.

As a consequence, an intergovernmental conference was held in London in April—May 1954, in which 42 nations were represented. They were equivalent to the owners of 95 percent of the world's shipping tonnage. The delegations all agreed this problem was a serious one and that a practical solution must be found to rid the beaches and seas of oil. As the problem in various countries is, and always will be, very different, opinions, of course, were equally varied. Some delegations merely wished to make recommendations; others desired total prohibition of the discharge of oil, or of oil-contaminated waters. However, the convention agreed, on May 12, 1954, on the main provision which was the prohibition of the deliberate discharge of oil, including the accidental discharge of oil and oily mixture.

At the conclusion of the conference, certain countries signed the convention, whose prohibitions were really comparatively severe, making considerable demands on every government. Representatives of a large number of countries signed the convention on behalf of their respective governments, subject, of course, to final ratification at home. Of

Along the Atlantic Coast, oil pollution periodically has killed thousands of birds such as these eiders

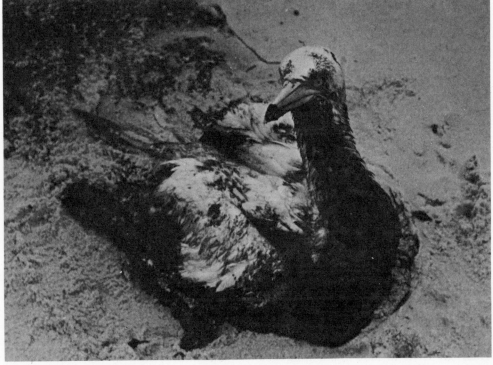

Helpless on the beach, an oil-soaked gannet is the victim of pollution

these, the signatories were Belgium, Canada, Denmark, Finland, the German Federal Republic, Greece, Yugoslavia, Italy, Bulgaria, Norway, Sweden, and the United Kingdom. After that, the following countries also signed: Ceylon, France, Republic of Ireland, Japan, Mexico, the Netherlands, New Zealand, and the Soviet Union.   —J.F.

Pollution on the North American Coasts

During the winter of 1949—1950, a particularly bad year for the prevalence of floating oil, thousands of dead or dying seabirds were reported killed or incapacitated off the Atlantic Coast from Maine south to Florida. One observer on Long Island reported that he counted more than 400 oiled gannets, loons, grebes, Bonaparte's gulls, razor-billed auks, dovekies, and ducks on the beaches between Montauk Point and Coney Island. Another experienced Long Island observer said that the destruction of seabirds by oil in the winter of 1949—1950 was by far the greatest in his memory. Inland, the problem was particularly acute at Detroit, where thousands of ducks and other waterfowl were destroyed by oil sludge dumped into the Rouge River. A government employee stationed in Virginia reported that the waters of Hampton Roads, from Oil Point South to the mouth of the James River, were periodically and frequently deluged with fuel and bilge oils from the fleet of naval ships that anchored abreast of the naval base. The worst offenders were the great aircraft carriers, though all oil-burning vessels were more or less guilty. In past years this observer had seen dead ducks by the hundreds washed up in the seaweed at high-water mark.

Julian K. Potter, regional editor of *Audubon Field Notes* published by the National Audubon Society, reported that oil sludge was often dumped into the Delaware River in the Philadelphia area (and in Raritan Bay, New Jersey), with

devastating effect upon waterfowl wintering on the river and bay. He likened the yearly damage of floating oil to waterbirds as equal to the annual traffic-kill of landbirds.

Periodically, seabirds were killed by oil on the oceanic and harbor waters of the Atlantic Coast of Canada. During the winter of 1949—1950, serious oil pollution there killed eider ducks, old squaws, scoters, scaups, golden-eyes, black ducks, murres, black guillemots, puffins, loons, gulls, and cormorants.

An ornithologist from the Pacific Coast said that damage to seabirds by oil had always been a problem there, but that tremendous numbers of birds killed had seldom been noted, possibly because of a lack of observers along the little-populated Pacific Coast of Washington and Oregon. Oil accidentally discharged in Seattle's waterfront had caused a heavy kill of waterbirds in January 1950. Species killed were common murres, pigeon guillemots, rhinoceros auklets, and marbled murrelets. The carcasses of fur seals, killed by oil, were washed up on the coasts of Washington and Oregon that winter.   J.K.T.

Saving Birds Polluted by Oil

Oil fuel, so widely used to power ships, machinery, and heating systems, has one major disadvantage: instead of clean ash it produces an insoluble tar-like waste that is too often allowed to pollute tidal rivers and the sea itself.

But not all the blame for oil pollution lies at the doors of industrial and shipping interests; the terrible decimation of ships in the submarine warfare of World War II left a legacy of sunken tankers lying beneath the Atlantic, many with their keel tanks still intact. Immersion in water slows the process of rusting considerably, and it is estimated that 15 to 20 years may pass before sea pressure finally bursts the steel casings to release hundreds of gallons of imprisoned oil. This comes to the surface and

Bird populations have been seriously diminished in areas where oil wells and re-fineries are abundant

spreads over an area of several miles, running like quicksilver to form tarry masses that carry impartially a cargo of weeds, wreakage, and seabirds.

This is merely a digest of the story that culminates in the arrival on British shores of many pitifully disabled wild-fowl, and occasionally, of the wholesale massacre of birds, like the one that oc-curred in the Baltic Sea when German observers reported that rafts of oil lying out at sea contained more than 30,000 birds.

In global terms, the endeavor to end oil pollution is in the hands of the In-ternational Committee for Bird Preserva-tion and the related International Convention. For individual bird con-servationists there remains the job of saving a few individual birds and re-turning them, clean and fit, to their natural lives.

So little is known about the care of seabirds that each one treated provides an opportunity for research and dis-covery, not only into ways and means of cleaning and reviving them but also their inherent habits and intelligence, and capacity for adapting themselves to a domestic life that is foreign to them. While some birds are so lightly affected by the oil that they can be released almost at once, probably 75 out of every 100 cast ashore are already dead or on the point of death. It is the remainder with some hope of eventual recovery that provides the interest and the challenge.

Congestion of the lungs, exposure, and starvation are the killers of oiled birds. In the course of the last few years a pattern of treatment has been developed that is often successful. First, cleaning the oiled feathers is forgotten for 24 hours, and during this time efforts are aimed entirely at warming and drying the victim and persuading it to take some food. A wad of cotton wool is tucked under each wing and then the whole bird is swathed in cotton wool, leaving only the bill and eyes uncovered. Then it is placed in an open box in a room temperature of as near 70° F. as possible.

A bird with any hope of survival will soon liven up and generate heat in its woolen cocoon, and this in turn will cause the wet feathers to steam and the moisture is absorbed by the wool. Warmth is so essential because in nature, water never penetrates the feathers to the skin, and, when in this case, it does, severe physical shock to the bird results.

As soon as it feels really warm, a little food can be given the bird. For divers, such as razor-billed auks and murres, this should consist of thin, finger-length slices of raw fish. One slice will be enough for the first feeding, and it should contain a capsule of halibut-liver, or other concentrated fish oil hidden in the food. Very few birds will accept the initial feed voluntarily, and so it must be gently forced by prying open the bill with the forefinger and thumb of the left hand, and slipping in the morsel of fish with the right. This is not so complicated in practice as it appears in print.

Once fed the bird can be left quiet in its woolen bed for several hours and by then it should be dry. If it has the strength to stand it may like to be uncovered and allowed to flap its wings, but on no account must it preen the polluted feathers, because in so doing, fuel oil may be swallowed by the bird. This will work still further against its chances of recovery. Any bird that is found wandering on the beach with oil on its breast feathers, should be given a dose of creamy milk to neutralize poisonous matter that it may have swallowed.

The next day the job of cleaning off the oil is begun. Originally a bath of warm water and detergent suds was recommended, however, it has since been learned that detergents are harmful to birds' feathers; and some people suggested that lard should be used to melt the tar before washing. The simplest and most effective removing agent is fuller's earth of prepared chalk, used as a kind of dry shampoo which can be rinsed out of the oiled bird's feathers after about 12 hours. It needs to be rubbed in thoroughly, though gently, with particular attention to clotted quills in the flight and tail feathers. Rinsing of the bird should be done in lukewarm water and it must be redried to avoid chills. Cleaning can be repeated at two-day intervals until the feathers are clear of oil. Although some stains may remain, these are harmless and will wear off in time.

A murre will accept these attentions philosophically, but with a razor-billed auk, it is wiser to wear light gloves as these birds can carve a neat slice out of one's finger with no trouble.

But for a really tough customer the gannet takes the prize. Birds, nervously on the defensive, can usually be coaxed with a soft voice and slow, gentle handling, but the gannet is an all-out attacker, able to sever a finger with one chop of its bill. However, with a lightly oiled gannet, a swift grasp can

A razor-billed auk, saved from oil pollution, eagerly accepts pieces of fish from its rescuer

get hold of the bird's neck just behind the head and render it temporarily harmless so that an assistant can pull a thick stocking over its bill and head, tying it firmly but not too tightly round the neck. Once in the dark the bird will relax and allow any treatment. The only advantage to a gannet is that when it gapes its bill in rage, a fish can be inserted and in this way it will soon learn to accept food. It prefers whole fish and can swallow up to six 8-ounce herrings at one meal; these must be of-

fered head first. A handy implement for the purpose is a pair of old-fashioned brass coal tongs.

Swans rescued from oiled waters may be equally dangerous at first but they can become very docile and friendly. Wild ducks are intelligent and easy to manage, though inclined to nervousness. Gulls, too are nice creatures but possessors of the maddening habit of accepting a cropful of food and then turning their backs and regurgitating the lot. This is a purely nervous reaction, used by the bird in the wild when it lightens its load before take-off if it is threatened by a predator.

Each bird has its own charm, but all share one disability: When they are otherwise clean and strong, they develop "wet-feather," and neither the cause nor the cure of this disorder is yet known. In effect the bird loses buoyancy and waterproofing and is unable to float on water. The cause bears no relation to the cleaning process because injured seabirds suffer equally with oiled ones. The British Wildfowl Trust has introduced a theory that "wet-feather" may be due to stress, a condition that can only be cured by the bird itself as it becomes adapted to a new environment and mode of living; when by degrees it can learn to live an aquatic life once more and a return to full freedom is possible. But present knowledge rests entirely on theory, and there is a wide field open for research into this problem.
—K.T.

Recommended Reading

Birds and Floating Oil—Roger T. Peterson. *Audubon Magazine* July-August 1942.
Oil and the California Murre—Frances Houldson. *Audubon Magazine* March-April 1952.
Oil on the Sea—Dillon Ripley. *Audubon Magazine* March-April 1942.
A Sea-bird Tragedy. *Bird-Lore* March-April 1930.

OKEECHOBEE
Lake Okeechobee Sanctuary

Though encircled by a highway, and more than halfway dyked, with limitless fields of cane and truck about its southern and eastern rims, Florida's Lake Okeechobee, second largest freshwater lake in the United States, is largely unknown to the average tourist who glimpses its wide waters. Nor do the transient vegetable pickers, crop growers and shippers themselves know it well. Only the fishermen, that hardy group of natives to whom heavy toil and exposure are daily grinds, understand its moods and erratic, often treacherous waters. It is a shallow lake in the.

Lake Okeechobee

main, and therefore subject to sudden squalls and storms; when infrequent hurricanes sweep across it, it is overwhelming in its wrath. Everything about it is big, and to many who see it, strange and somewhat forbidding in its vastness. To others who have witnessed its eccentricities, its combination of tranquillity and violence, its undoubted beauty and teeming wildlife, there is a fascination about the Big Water.

Like the mysterious Everglades, which for centuries it fed and nourished, the lake has changed much in recent years, but it still retains that wilderness quality, that limitless reach of horizons and capricious interpretation of the moods of nature, that one sometimes gains from seeing the Great Plains.

While perfectly open water for much of its huge expanse, Lake Okeechobee does have a few large islands which are cultivated and inhabited to some extent, these lying off the southern and southwestern shoreline. However, many smaller ones appear elsewhere, as off the northern rim, and are nothing more than stretches of cane, heavy grasses, and cattails, with no dry land whatever. These are known to local Floridians as "reefs." Occasionally, beds of willows appear in this growth, and great patches of water hyacinths, lilies, and similar aquatic plants hide the water for acres and become a glory of bloom in the spring. Amid these the reptilian life of the lake flourishes, represented by the steadily diminishing alligator and numerous snakes, among which occurs the venomous water (cottonmouth) moccasin. Sandy bars, created by dredging in the construction of the great dyke erected as a hurricane barrier, appear here and there. On these nest thriving colonies of terns.

Remarkable examples of bird distribu-

The black-necked stilt sits on its nest with its 10 inch legs doubled under its body

tion exist in Florida, and are nowhere better illustrated than in the Okeechobee area. Birds occur there that are not only largely absent from any other part of the state, but the whole country as well. Others live there that are represented in other parts of the United States, but in very distant parts of it, with none occurring in between. Examples of the former are the glossy ibis and Everglade kite; of the latter, the caracara, burrowing owl, and Florida (sandhill) crane.

The lake itself is highly conducive to a large bird population because of the presence of all essentials necessary to a bird's existence—an abundance of food, water, and cover. Herons thrive there because of the swarming minnows, frogs, and small snakes; ibises congregate about the lake because of the many crayfishes; ducks find extensive beds of aquatic plants, roots, tubers, and seeds. Gulls, terns, shorebirds, white pelicans, ospreys, and eagles, aid in maintaining the balance of finny life amid the waters. Such highly specialized feeders as the Everglade kite and limpkin are constantly supplied with their chosen item of diet, the large freshwater snail, *Pomacea caliginosa* (*See under Kite and under Limpkin*).

The only river of any consequence that empties into the lake is the Kissimmee (accent on the second syllable), and from its mouth on the northern shore the marshes and willows, following its many bends, also harbor a birdlife similar to that of the lake itself.

The State of Florida owns much of the shore and marsh areas of Lake Okeechobee. The maintenance of a sanctuary on a large section of the northwestern shore of the lake has been the responsibility of the National Audubon Society. It has been posted and patrolled the year round, and it is this extensive block of marsh and water that is known as the Okeechobee Sanctuary. Patrol of the area is carried on by an Audubon warden who has travelled by boat over the waterways and overland in a jeep.

Probably this sanctuary has been known to more visitors than any other in the whole chain of southern refuges of the National Audubon Society. There, during the winters of 1940 and 1941 were begun the two-day trips that constituted the Okeechobee Wildlife Tours of the National Audubon Society.

Because of unwise drainage, the advances of civilization, and a variety of other encroachments on the Lake Okeechobee area, some forms of its birdlife have their last stronghold there. It is imperative that they be given every opportunity to survive and increase. This is particularly true of such species as the Everglade kite and the glossy ibis; also the limpkin, that strange combination of crane and rail with the amazing voice (*See under Limpkin*).

The status of other birds at Lake Okeechobee is more firmly established. All the herons of Florida live about the lake with the exception of the great white heron and even it sometimes strays northward to Lake Okeechobee from its normal haunts among the Florida Keys.

Similarly, ibises nest on the grassy reefs or in nearby cypress hammocks. Caracaras search for turtle eggs and snakes along the Lakeport Road (State Highway 29), and to see them outside of this area, one must travel to the central and southern coast of Texas. Burrowing owls pop up between the cattle guards of this fascinating highway, and to find them outside of Florida would necessitate a journey west of the Mississippi River. Riding in stately splendor on the lake itself, or wheeling in tremendous circles above the marshes, squadrons of white pelicans catch the sun on their glistening plumage, although they never nest east of the Mississippi River, and only rarely east of the Rocky Mountains. Yet these great birds winter regularly in Florida and may be counted on as appearing in at least three parts of the state during the cold months.

Situated as it is, in the interior of Florida, one would not ordinarily expect many seabirds or shorebirds about the lake. And yet black-necked stilts and dowitchers; pectoral sandpipers and kill-deer; yellowlegs and common, or Wilson's snipe are seen seasonally, as well as others of the plover and sandpiper tribe. Herring, ring-billed, and laughing gulls are common on the lake; gull-billed and Forster's terns are dwarfed by royal and Caspian terns, and Florida cormorants, water turkeys, and pied-billed grebes are also seen on the lake.

Among the landbirds variety is also marked and one is rarely out of sight of boat-tailed grackles, loggerhead shrikes, ground doves, and southern meadowlarks. In the cypress "heads," where tall, gray-green trunks soar sky-ward, bannered with swinging moss, yellow-throated warblers and tufted tit-mice live. The "cabbage hammocks," those great islands of palmettos amid seas of prairie grass, harbor pileated woodpeckers and Florida barred owls.

Pinelands echo to the notes of towhees, cardinals, and brown-headed nuthatches, while mockingbirds pour out their match-less melody everywhere.

As for hawks—it makes one feel there are some left after all. What would one think of seeing 27 red-shouldered hawks in 20 miles? And 37 sparrow hawks in 13 miles? Occasional red-tailed hawks, rarer duck hawks, numberless vultures of both species, frequent eagles, and even wandering rough-legged hawks are to be seen daily. Truly this is not only bird country, but especially hawk country.

Last there are many kinds of ducks to be seen on Lake Okeechobee. Okeechobee does not boast as great an assortment of species of waterfowl as in other parts of their southern wintering range but individuals are numerous of those that do occur. Lesser scaup and ring-necked ducks usually predominate, followed by pintail and baldpates. Blue-

Saw palmettos are common in Lake Okeechobee Sanctuary

*Water hyacinth chokes many of the
Lake Okeechobee Sanctuary waterways*

winged teal and shovellers are not uncommon, and now and then a few can-
vasbacks appear. The wood duck and
Florida (black) duck occur on the lake
the year round.

The Okeechobee Sanctuary thus has
fulfilled numerous needs and afforded
many people the opportunity of seeing
what an Audubon refuge is and how the
wardens have performed. Rare, locally
distributed birds have been under constant watch and their nesting, feeding,
and roosting places patrolled. Other
birds living in close proximity have had
the same care, and transient and winter
birds also have come under the protective custody seasonally. All the while,
there has been a steadily growing understanding of the vital need of conservation of native wildlife and realization
by visitors and people living in the
area of the value of the Lake Okeechobee
area as a great wildlife sanctuary.

—A.S. Jr.

*The long legs of the caracara suggest
that it is largely terrestrial*

OKEFENOKEE NATIONAL WILDLIFE REFUGE

Location—Southeastern Georgia
Size—517 square miles
Mammals—Black bears, bobcats, white-tailed deer, bats, opossums, skunks, otters, minks
Birdlife—American egrets, red-shouldered hawks, sandhill cranes, ibises, storks, anhingas, herons, ducks, many songbirds
Plants—Maidencanes, floating hearts, tall pitcher plants, mosses, bladderworts, chain ferns, white bays, live, scrub, and water oaks, magnolias, slash pines, gums, bald cypresses
Accommodations—Meals, cabins, boats, guides at nearby Stephen Foster Camp and Cornelia Camp
Headquarters—Post Office Building, Waycross, Georgia

In the southeastern corner of Georgia lies a magnificent watery wilderness, the famous Okefenokee Swamp. Covering 600 to 700 square miles, and varying in width from 18 to 30 miles, this great swamp has been formed behind a low barrier athwart the sandy, flat South Atlantic coastal plain. Behind the barrier the waters flowing from the northward are retained upon the broad, low-lying, and nearly level plain and are eventually fed into the two outflowing streams. These are the St. Mary's River, which flows into the Atlantic Ocean, and the Suwannee River, which finds its way in a southwesterly direction into the Gulf of Mexico.

Okefenokee is actually a vast bog (*see Bog*), unique in many respects as to its geologic origin and history, and justly renowned for its remarkably rich plant-life and animal life. It is a wildlife paradise beyond compare. Within its vast, watery haven some of the rarest birds and mammals native to the southeastern United States find sanctuary; for most of Okefenokee is now one of the numerous units in the far-flung system of national refuges maintained by the Fish and Wildlife Service of the United States Department of the Interior.

The eastern portion of the swamp is more or less an open bog, with innumerable cypress-studded islets and some large pine-clad islands, presenting a scene of incomparable grandeur, possibly unique among the world's landscapes. Native people of the region have given these grand, open, marshlike areas the curious designation of *prairies*. The shallow waters overspreading vast areas are filled with a luxuriant growth of marsh and aquatic plants. Spatterdocks, or bonnets, *Nymphaea macrophylla;* white water lilies, *Castalia odorata;* golden clubs, or "never-wets," *Orontium aquaticum;* arrow arums, or wampee, *Peltandra virginica;* floating hearts, *Nymphoides aquaticum;* maiden cane, *Panicum hemitomon;* and many other water-dwelling plants grow in rank profusion in the dark, sphagnum-filled water. Okefenokee folk have long navigated the prairies in their narrow, flat-bottomed boats, propelled by pushing them forward from the stern with a long pole.

Westward, Okefenokee becomes more and more a true swamp where the waters are shallower and tree growth much more dominant. Formerly, most of this section was covered by a dense stand of cypress and extensive hammocks of bays and magnolias; but over the greater part of the region the big timber has long since been removed. Evidence of the days when the great cypresses were cut and hauled away is apparent in the cypress pilings that ramify the swamp and over which the logging trams once carried the huge logs to the sawmill.

During the heyday of timber operations a town of some six hundred inhabitants flourished on Billy's Island. A few stately palmettoes and a tiny grave plot long overgrown and forgotten, are all that remain of the community abandoned in the early 1900's. Civilization passed this way—and left its marks—but nature is rapidly reclaiming her domain in the Okefenokee, the Indian

The predominant vegetation in Okefenokee National Wildlife Refuge is bald cypress and Spanish moss

Guided boat tours at Okefenokee National Wildlife Refuge introduce visitors to the plants and animals living there

name of which means *Land of the Trembling Earth.*

At one time a huge sum of money and much arduous labor were fruitlessly expended in an effort to drain this great swamp. A canal was dug from near Camp Cornelia on the swamp's eastern side to a point some twelve or fourteen miles into the interior. It was proposed to drain off the waters into the St. Mary's River through this canal but it was discovered that the water was actually flowing westward in the canal, into the swamp, and toward the Suwannee River. It was a gross engineering blunder for which all lovers of wildlife can be thankful. Today the canal hardly appears to have been dug at all, and it affords easy access by boat into the magnificent prairie regions of the eastern portion of the swamp.

The largest bodies of open water in Okefenokee Swamp are located to the west. Probably, these so-called "lakes" are wider and deeper stretches of the winding Suwannee River; but they are natural gems, resplendently mirroring the sky, the passing clouds, and the trees and shrubs that crowd their shoreless margins. In the surrounding forests of cypresses, gums, bays, and magnolias —with their pendant streamers of Spanish moss—dwell bears, raccoons, bobcats, and many lesser furred creatures of the wilderness. There the cries of the red-shouldered hawk can be heard almost constantly by day; and from twilight to dawn the calls of the great horned owl and Florida barred owl echo and re-echo through the mysterious depths of the watery jungles. There, too, one of the mighty alligators of the swamp may bellow during the spring mating season, for 'gators—and big ones —are still prominent among the swamp dwellers (*See Alligator*).

Billy's Lake, the largest body of open water in the swamp, is 3½ miles long and 100 to 250 yards wide. It is easily accessible from the town of Fargo, Georgia, on the west side of the swamp. One can never forget the sheer beauty of Billy's Lake as he may see it on a fine October morning. Its surface will be as placid as a huge plate-glass mirror. The slender, grayish-colored shafts of the bordering cypresses seem to project both upward toward the sky and downward into the dark watery depths.

Pileated woodpeckers drum on the bony, seasoned masts of dead cypresses. Catbirds and Carolina wrens call ceaselessly in the dense thickets. An occasional cardinal flashes through the shrubs of titi and dahoon. As one slowly paddles up the lake, wood ducks spring from the little coves and utter their characteristic *who-eek* as they fly into the fastnesses of the forest. A water turkey or anhinga, may come across the lake, alternately flapping its white-patched wings and then sailing. Common, or American, egrets wade about in the shallow, bonnet-strewn bays, searching for minnows and frogs and acting as though they are admiring their own reflections in the water. But the grandest sight of all may come as the visitor turns his boat into one of the little bays and a flock of wood storks take to the air, slowly circling above the cypress spires.

The boat run, or canal, after leaving Billy's Lake near its upper end, traverses some of the most beautiful swamp country to be found in the Okefenokee—or anywhere else. The run, a narrow, watery trail through the cypress forest, is flanked on either side by impenetrable thickets of "hurrah bushes," *Pieris nitida;* titi, *Cyrilla racemosa;* dahoon holly, *Ilex cassine;* fetterbrush, *Eubotrys racemosa;* and other swamp shrubs. Intermixed with the dominant cypress are other swamp trees—the red maple, *Acer rubrum;* sweet bay, *Persea pubescens;* white bay, *Magnolia virginiana;* loblolly bay, *Gordonia lasianthus.* Occasional bull bays, or magnolias, *Magnolia grandiflora,* occur in the hummocks. This is one of the most beautiful of the native trees, with their thick, dark green, lus-

An American egret stands watch over its young. Protected in the Okefenokee National Wildlife Refuge, it has nothing to fear but natural predators

trous leaves and rusty-colored undersurfaces. In late spring it produces waxy white, lemon-scented blossoms approximately eight inches wide.

Everywhere on little hummocks of sphagnum are clumps of cinnamon, royal, and chain ferns. Every now and then the run widens out a little, creating small shallow-water openings of bonnets, pickerelweed, and the interesting aquatic plant the natives call the "never-wet." When one submerges the pointed, oval-shaped, bluish-green leaves, they glow with a rich reddish-golden iridescence. Let them bob up again and they are bone dry, for they shed water like the feathers of a duck's back.

After a few miles of tortuous travel through this strangely beautiful world of trees, shrubs, vines, ferns, and mosses, and of mysterious lights and shadows, one emerges upon the broader, tranquil waters of Minnie's Lake. Like Billy's Lake, though considerably smaller, Minnie's Lake contains reflections of moss-draped cypresses and billowy, white clouds. Okefenokee lakes are all

superlative, natural mirrors and they harbor some truly gigantic largemouth bass and huge populations of other species such as jackfishes, catfishes, and "perch," or warmouth. Wherever one goes, turtles of several kinds may be seen basking in the sun along the shores or sliding off half-submerged logs. What may at first appear to be a dark, floating log is perhaps an alligator. Very artfully it will sink from sight but its course toward a deep 'gator hole is plainly visible in a string of bubbles.

At the upper end of Minnie's Lake the traveler enters another narrow boat run and soon crosses the wide, sunny expanse of Floyd's Island Prairie. There, invariably, one will see egrets and little blue herons, and possibly wood storks or sandhill cranes. A female wood duck may make quite a commotion in the shallow water, acting as though her wings are hopelessly crippled, while her brood cleverly conceal themselves among the sedges, pickerelweeds, arums, and paintroots. Over in a nearby island a pair of red-shouldered hawks pierce the stillness with their shrilly repeated *kee-*

Many species of ducks migrate to Okefenokee National Wildlife Refuge in winter

you! A green heron rises from a patch of cattails and on slowly flapping wings heads out across the marsh. Up on the tip of a small cypress tree a male red-winged blackbird utters his *oak-a-lee* and spreads his wings to display his scarlet and buff epaulets. Overhead a number of turkey vultures slowly describe great circles as they effortlessly mount higher and higher into a blue sky filled with cottony masses of cumulus clouds.

Soon again one comes into the cypress zone and the boat run enters wide, deep, dark water once more. Big Water, with its forest-rimmed borders, miraculously unfolds itself. There is the very heart of the Okefenokee with its solitude – primitive, grand, and eternal. One pauses to listen to the songs of birds; to the wild, ringing notes of prothonotary warblers emanating from dark, tangled thickets; and the buzzing trills of parula warblers reaching down from the moss-festooned boughs overhead. The clear,

sweet voices of Carolina wrens ring from one end of the lake to the other. An Acadian flycatcher on a nearby magnolia bough explosively utters its emphatic *swee-up.* Lordly pileated woodpeckers cross and recross the lake, going from one wooded shore to the other and occasionally making the forests ring with their resounding calls. Frequently one hears the reverberating sounds being beaten by pileated woodpeckers and occasionally catches glimpses of their black-and-white bodies and scarlet-crested heads. Today the pileated is king of the woodpecker clan, but there was a day when the even larger ivory-billed woodpecker was not uncommon in the Okefenokee wilderness. Perhaps, somewhere in its vast expanse, a few of them may still exist although nobody has seen one there for many years. When the stumps of the swamp were gigantic virgin cypresses, the great ivory-bills undoubtedly lived and nested

The anhinga is a resident of Okefenokee National Wildlife Refuge. It feeds on fishes and other small aquatic animals

*The raccoon finds an abundant supply of small aquatic animals—its favorite diet—
in Okefenokee National Wildlife Refuge*

among the moss-draped curtains of their lofty crowns.

After following the canal for a couple of miles, one may turn northward into another boat run which leads to the grand expanse of Chase Prairie.

Chase Prairie—with its acres of bonnets, white water lilies, and never-wets, and its innumerable islets studded with grotesque, mossy-tressed cypresses was once described by the American naturalist James G. Needham as "one of the most remarkable landscapes in the world." It is exquisite, too, with its masses of little violet-purple blossoms that the bladderworts, *Utricularia purpurea*, hold above the dark, watery bed of the prairie. The growth of this plant is so extensive, even in the boat run, that the outboard motor is useless and one resorts to poling or paddling the boat.

Wood ducks, singly and in twos and threes, get up before the boat and wing their way across the sun-flooded aquatic meadow. White egrets on lazily flapping snowy pinions occasionally alight atop a cypress and, with apparent curiosity, watch one's progress across the prairie. Okefenokee is a winter refuge for waterfowl—often great numbers of mallards, black ducks, blue-winged teal, ringnecks, and lesser numbers of several other species that arrive there from the inhospitable, frozen marshes of the North.

From afar, across Chase Prairie, one may see on Floyd's Island, tall longleaf pines, a few veterans left from a magnificent forest which fell before the saw and axe years ago. On Floyd's Island, as on most of the other sizable islands of the Okefenokee, are burial mounds left by prehistoric man. Large human skeletons, pottery, and various artifacts were exhumed from one of these mounds when excavations were made for the logging railroad into the swamp. Who the builders were still remains a mystery, for the Seminole Indians that once lived in Okefenokee Swamp claimed that the mounds were built before their time.

A Seminole village existed on Floyd's Island prior to 1838, the year in which General Floyd crossed the swamp and drove Billy Bowlegs and his band of Seminoles out of their hunting grounds.

Today the Okefenokee Swamp is almost entirely within the boundaries of the Okefenokee National Wildlife Refuge. As a winter refuge for hosts of migratory waterfowl it is easily the peer of most other refuge areas set aside primarily for that purpose. But Okefenokee is more than a waterfowl refuge. It is a haven for the alligator and otter, the white-tailed deer and Florida black bear, the raccoon and bobcat. Its prairies are home and sanctuary for egrets and ibises, and the deep swamp forests are the domain of the water turkey and pileated woodpecker. All Americans cherish the hope that the majestic sandhill cranes that live in this swamp shall forever sound their trumpets across these magnificent expanses. They hope they will continue to nest unmolested in the watery fastnesses; that the graceful swallow-tailed kites shall continue to sweep the skies above the swamp and ospreys to build their lofty cradles in its isolated cypress snags. With the passing of the years, nature will erase the man-made scars and restore primeval grandeur to the great swamp. She is already rebuilding the forests of pines on the high dry islands, and the cypresses in the swamps. Far from being a dismal morass where perils lurk on every hand, Okefenokee is a land of manifold charms. It is a land of serene and lovely vistas—an incomparable paradise of woods, and waters, and wildlife—and a place of haunting mystery.   —W.G.

OLIVE

The fruiting shrub that gave its name to the widespread family Oleaceae is a native to the Mediterranean Basin. Introduced into California where the climate is very similar to its native habitat, it is cultivated in groves for the drupes, hard-shelled fruits surrounded by a fleshy, edible substance.

North American relatives of the olive are ash, fringe tree, devilwood, swamp privet, and desert olive. The flowers of the trees and shrubs in this family have two stamens, the leaves are opposite, and the fruit is variable.

Other important Eurasian species of this group are lilacs and privets, both widely planted as ornamentals in North America.   —G.B.S.

OLYMPIC NATIONAL PARK

Location—Northwestern Washington
Size—1,321 square miles
Mammals—Mountain lions, black bears, mountain goats, beavers, mountain beavers, marmots, rabbits, squirrels, seals
Birdlife — Bald eagles, golden eagles, woodpeckers, grouse; 140 species of nesting birds, many migrants
Plants—Sitka spruces, alpine firs, Douglas-firs, silver firs, western red cedars, western hemlocks, rhododendrons, madrones, many wild flowers

The Olympic Mountains, occupying much of the interior of Washington's Olympic Peninsula, were once a lava bed on the ocean floor. Geological uplift followed by erosion and glacial action formed the contours of this rugged land of scattered peaks. The highest, Mount Olympus, is 7,954 feet above sea level.

The warm waters of the Japanese Current run south along the coast of Washington and cause the formation of dense clouds. The moisture-laden air rides up over the mountains, losing most of its water vapor in the form of rain or snow—nearly 12 feet annually on the western slope of the mountains. Some

of the coniferous trees growing along these western slopes grow to over 200 feet in height. Their bark is green with mosses and fern thickets growing at their bases.

No roads run through the park, but there are more than 600 miles of trails.
Accommodations—Lodges, inns, and campgrounds
Headquarters—Port Angeles, Washington

OPOSSUM
Other Common Names—Possum, polecat
Scientific Name—*Didelphis virginiana*
Family—Didelphiidae (opossum family)
Order—Marsupialia
Size—Body length, 15 to 20 inches; tail, 9 to 13 inches; weight, 4 to 12 pounds
Range—Eastern United States from central New England to Florida and westward to Wisconsin, Colorado, and Texas. Introduced into Pacific Coast areas

Because of its nocturnal nature, few people realize that the opossum is distributed over a large part of the United States. Not so many years ago only the southern United States was its homeland. But since the turn of the century the so-called Virginia opossum has emigrated both north and westward.

Whereas only a rare straggler was reported in Ontario before 1900 it is now in process of establishing residence there. Saskatchewan, too, is witnessing its slow advance; so are southern Vermont and New Hampshire. But its most surprising migration is to the Pacific Coast—to Los Angeles in particular. More than 1,000 a year are picked up by the authorities in Hollywood alone, and opossum traffic casualties in the city are numerous.

That the opossum should be mistaken for a giant rat is not surprising. One of its best descriptions, and possibly the earliest, was written in 1608 by Captain John Smith, founder of Virginia, who said: "An opossum hath a head like a swine, a taile like a rat, and is of the bignes of a cat. Under her belly she hath a bagge wherein she lodgeth, carrieth, and sucketh her young."

That "bagge" in which young opossums are carried and suckled places this fascinating animal in a class by itself: the marsupial. It is a member of the order to which kangaroos and koala bears belong, but the only marsupial on the North American continent north of Mexico. A marsupial is a mammal whose young are born at such an undeveloped state that the mother is obliged to carry them about in her abdominal pouch (*marsupium*) for several weeks.

Thus hazards begin early in the life of opossums. Less than two weeks after their parents mate, the young are born—blind, deaf, hairless, and so small that two dozen would just fill a teaspoon, and, they weigh only a fraction of an ounce each. Curiously, their tiny forelegs, developed out of all proportion to the rest of their embryonic bodies, are sharply clawed, and for good reason. Nature has imposed a cruel aptitude test for these little creatures—to fail it is to die.

As soon as baby opossums are born they must find their way into the mother's abdominal pouch. Having forelegs with claws enables the newly born to drag themselves by an overhead stroke as in swimming—across the two or three inches of curly abdominal fur separating them from the pouch entrance, thence up and in where milk, warmth, and security await them. This they do by themselves with little or no assistance from the mother.

Merely finding sanctuary in the pouch is by no means all of their problem. The usual number of teats on the North American opossum is 13—nine is the minimum, seventeen the maximum—and her brood is ordinarily more numerous, sometimes 25. First come, first served is the rule. Once safely inside, each baby

Gigantic Sitka spruce trees dwarf a horseman at Olympic National Park, Washington

The opossum's scaly, prehensile tail gives it the appearance of an overgrown rat

opossum must find a life-giving nipple, then clamp onto it tenaciously. This it accomplishes by pressing the nipple against the roof of its mouth with its powerful tongue, pressing so firmly that only a vigorous yank by one's fingers will detach it.

Babies arriving too late for a nipple of their own must perish of starvation and exposure, and such hazards usually reduce the litter to seven or eight before weaning is over. In the meantime, the mother is obliged to forage in the woods for food and protect herself and her ever present family as best she can. The adult male opossum of the pair shows no interest in his mate or family after mating is accomplished.

After eight or nine weeks in the pouch, and attached to nipples all but the last few days, the youngsters develop fully. The young opossum, the size of a mouse, is ready and eager to move into the open, to travel about on mother's back while clinging to her fur. Such a traveling family group of opossums is one of the most amusing sights in nature, certainly one of her most unique ways of animal transportation.

One summer evening on Chicago's North Shore, a mother opossum was seen to emerge from the roots of a tall elm tree where she had been using an abandoned woodchuck hole for her nest. Clinging tightly to tiny handfuls of fur, four beady-eyed, gray-furred babies were hanging on one side of her back, three on the opposite side while behind her, three less fortunate youngsters—one of them an albino (*see Albino*) waddled under their own power, clinging to her tail or one another's tail for guidance.

The riders, swaying this way or that with her flatfooted trudging, were gazing about like country youngsters on their first trip to town. All seemed to be enjoying the journey immensely.

At twelve or thirteen weeks the babies

are still dependent on their mother, but will soon begin brief exploratory visits into the bush. For probably another fortnight they continue association with the family, then, growing more self-reliant, they seek their fortunes elsewhere, becoming what naturalist Ernest Thompson Seton called "fat hermits of the low woods." They are indeed solitary animals; no naturalist has yet reported seeing two wild adult opossums together, even during the breeding season.

Opossums are omnivorous. They eat insects, snakes, and carrion—even rats and mice when the slow-moving opossum is lucky enough to capture them. According to mammalogists who have studied the opossum's feeding habits, it does not live entirely on animal food, but a mixed diet that includes grains, seeds, and fruit, especially persimmons.

During the summer, however, insects are the most important item of its menu. Garbage pails and dumps attract it and stealthy visits to poultry sheds are sometimes charged against the opossum. No doubt, it may kill birds occasionally and feed on eggs and nestlings.

Caught in the open, an opossum rolls on its side and "plays dead." If dealt a sharp tap, it growls or hisses and makes a weak attempt to escape. Failing, it becomes semi-rigid, assuming what psychiatrists call a catatonic state in which it may be swung by the tail and tossed gently aside, without a flutter of its eyelids. Lying on its side, limbs partly extended, mouth open and drooling, teeth bared in a grin, tongue extended and touching the ground, eyes open but filmed, the opossum puts on a convincing death act. More significant, its heart beat and respiration actually diminish to the extent that neither may be readily detected.

Some scientists attribute this apparent coma to shock, some say fright. Whatever the cause it may suddenly revive after danger has passed, and attempt to escape. Playing 'possum, incidentally,

At eight weeks of age, eight opossums just fill a teaspoon

The fruit of the persimmon tree is a favorite food of the opossum

has also been attributed to kangaroos, certain foxes, the Australian dingo, and several birds and insects.

Carl Hartman, a world authority on opossums has suggested they are the least intelligent of all mammals. But William T. James, professor of psychology at the University of Georgia, discov-

*As many as 18 opossums are born at a time. Of this number only seven to nine,
usually 8, survive the period of pouch life*

ered that opossums may be smarter than has been supposed. James devised a laboratory cage having two compartments separated by a door with latches not too complicated for a smart little animal to open. In the evening he put an opossum in the box, dropped food in the adjoining compartment, closed and latched the connecting door, set up a camera and went to bed. During the night, the opossum solved the problem of the latch and how to dine. In doing so it set off the camera and flash, photographing itself in the act.

In one test that James offered this animal, a pole on the floor of its cage had to be pushed before the latch would open. Gradually, the investigator made the test more complicated. In the second test a single latch was on the door; in the third there were two latches. And in the fourth, the lower latch had to be lowered before the upper would function. The first three tests seemed elementary enough to the opossum; it took it 12 nights to solve the fourth. It finally gained its objective by breaking off both locks. From this James concluded that the opossum may be a lot smarter and more adaptable than had previously been suspected.

Unlike the skunk, porcupine, or weasel, the opossum has only meager means of defense. It is preyed upon by man, by hawks, owls, foxes, dogs, wolves, bobcats, ocelots, coyotes, and other carnivores. Its life expectancy is short; however, it has several adaptations which, with its great fecundity, have enabled it not only to survive but to expand its range immensely.

One advantage to its survival is the fact that it is normally active only at night. Much of its time, both day and night, is spent in lonely, lazy seclusion in tree cavities or burrows abandoned by other animals. Further, the opossum is an excellent tree climber, in fact an essentially arboreal creature when away from human habitations. In its climbing, it uses its feet with grasping toes that resemble a monkey's, and a scaly, prehensile tail used both for support and as aerial brakes. Its 50 sharp little teeth are more numerous than any other North American mammal's. Its sense of smell, so vital to good foraging, is exceptionally developed, and it has a surprising capacity for recovering from broken ribs and shoulders.

Perhaps the opossum is one of nature's best proofs that adaptability is more important to a wild animal in its wild environment than the gift of intelligence, by which man attempts to survive.

—R.B.W.

ORCHID

A genus of monocotyledons (plants with paralled veins in their leaves), orchids occur in all of the world's temperate and tropical climates. Some kinds grow from the soil and are called terrestrial orchids; others grow on the bark of trees, without harming the host, and are known as epiphytic orchids (*See Epiphyte*). There are probably more than 7,000 different species of orchids and many hybrids.

Every orchid has three petals, often large and colorful. Two of them are the same in shape and color, while the third is generally quite different. The sepals, either three or five, are as colorful as the petals in some species.

Lady's slipper

Pollination is by insects, and some species are so highly evolved that only one species, or perhaps one genus, of insect can perform the task. Nectar is the attraction: The third petal, or lip, of the flower is the landing platform; and a complex device within the plant deposits pollen on the back of the insect. When the insect enters another flower, the pollen comes in contact with the stigma and fertilization occurs. The seeds take a year to ripen, and as many as 800,000 of them are released from one seed capsule. These are transported by the wind. The minute number of seeds that find the right environment take up to twelve years to bloom.

Of the 300 or so wild orchids in the northern United States and southern Canada, the best known are the lady's slippers (*Cypripedium*), terrestrial plants of moist woodlands, and the green, white, or yellow fringed orchids that often grow in meadows and marshes. (*See Moccasin Flower*).

The species most generally used for corsages are the cattleyas, large and showy blooms originally from South America, but now raised commercially almost everywhere.   —G.B.S.

ORGAN PIPE CACTUS NATIONAL MONUMENT

Location—Southwestern Arizona
Size—516 square miles
Mammals—Desert bighorns, pronghorns, mule deer, whitetail deer, peccaries, coyotes, foxes, coatis, badgers, rabbits
Birdlife—Ravens, quail, white-winged doves, Inca doves, mourning doves, canyon wrens, cactus wrens, phainopeplas, vermilion flycatchers, roadrunners

Plants—Organ-pipe cacti, saguaros, senita cacti, hedgehog cacti, night-blooming cereuses, ocotillos, palo verdes, creosote bushes, mesquites, catclaws, desert willows (*See under Cactus*)

The unique flora of the Sonoran Desert is the chief attraction of this monument. Forty miles of road, in a meandering loop, penetrate the wilderness. Many of the plants and mammals are more typical of Mexico than of the United States.

Five short chains of rugged mountains are within the monument's boundaries, with a few peaks nearly 5,000 feet above sea level. Most of the terrain is flat or gently rolling.

Accommodations—Campgrounds within the monument, other facilities at Ajo, Arizona (18 miles)
Headquarters—Within the monument; address is Ajo, Arizona

Organ-pipe cactus has many columns that branch from its base